MW00438648

Preview Copy
Limited Edition

Psychology Astray is a masterpiece of clear thinking. Pope writes clearly, crisply, and provocatively. His examples are fabulous, and his down-to-earth style is readily accessible even to those with no formal training in psychology. This book teaches readers what good solid evidence is all about. Teachers and students, lawyers and judges, therapists and their patients, and families will all find the book immensely valuable.

**—Elizabeth Loftus, Ph.D., Professor of Psychology,
University of Washington, and author of *The Myth of Repressed Memory***

This is an outstanding book about memory, but it is much more; it is a fascinating lesson on how to think critically about research. As such, it should be read by everyone interested in psychology. . . . The cases, stories, and examples are funny, riveting, and memorable; they will provide helpful guides for evaluating future research. . . . Pope is an excellent scholar and effective teacher!

**—David Holmes, Ph.D., Professor of Psychology,
University of Kansas, and author of *Abnormal Psychology***

This well-written, lively, and thoughtful book is the best introduction I know to the pitfalls of reasoning that lie behind the egregious contemporary psychiatric misadventure variously titled "repressed memories," "traumatic memories of abuse," and "recovered memories" of sexual abuse. The author is an experienced psychiatric clinician and a first class psychiatric investigator who in this book has taken the time and effort to depict the deranged logic in the published studies proposing repressed memories. He has, as well, described what would constitute proper studies to identify or demolish this idea. I shall recommend this book to resident psychiatrists and medical students concerned about the foundations of psychiatry, but also I will recommend it to interested members of the public who wish to understand how psychiatry can go wrong and also how it can go right. A book of this sort has been long needed.

**—Paul R. McHugh, M.D., Henry Phipps Professor of Psychiatry and
Chief, Department of Psychiatry and Behavioral Sciences,
Johns Hopkins University School of Medicine**

The history of science is full of assumptions that later turn out to be false or at least misleading, and psychology is no exception. One such assumption concerns the repression of anxiety-including memories; another is that such repressions—assuming they occur at all—can be removed by hypnosis or various drugs. Dr. Pope's book critically examines the evidence for these assumptions, and throws doubt upon much of it. I recommend it as useful reading for students of psychology, especially those concerned with the evaluation of claims of recovered childhood memories.

**—Henry Gleitman, Ph.D., Professor of Psychology,
University of Pennsylvania, and author of *Psychology***

PSYCHOLOGY
ASTRAY

Other books by Harrison G. Pope, Jr., M.D.

Voices from the Drug Culture, 1971

The Road East, 1974

New Hope for Binge Eaters:
Advances in the Understanding and Treatment of Bulimia
with James I. Hudson, M.D., 1984

Other works edited by Harrison G. Pope, Jr., M.D.

The Psychobiology of Bulimia
with James I. Hudson, M.D., 1987

Use of Anticonvulsants in Psychiatry:
Recent Advances
with Susan L. McElroy, M.D., 1988

Other Upton Books publications

Confabulations:
Creating False Memories, Destroying Families
by Eleanor Goldstein with Kevin Farmer, 1992

True Stories of False Memories
by Eleanor Goldstein and Kevin Farmer, 1993

Beware the Talking Cure:
Psychotherapy May Be Hazardous to Your Mental Health
by Terence W. Campbell, Ph.D., 1994

Survivor Psychology:
The Dark Side of a Mental Health Mission
by Susan Smith, 1995

PSYCHOLOGY
ASTRAY

Fallacies in Studies of "Repressed Memory" and Childhood Trauma

Harrison G. Pope, Jr., M.D.

Upton
BOOKS

A division of

Social Issues Resources Series, Inc.
P.O. Box 2348
Boca Raton, FL 33427
1-800-232-7477 ● custserve@sirs.com

Library of Congress Cataloging-in-Publication Data

Pope, Harrison.
   Psychology astray: fallacies in studies of "repressed memory" and childhood trauma / by Harrison G. Pope, Jr., M.D.
     p. cm.
   Includes bibliographical references and index.
   ISBN 0-89777-149-4 : $12.95
   1. Repression (Psychology)—Research—Evaluation. 2. Psychic trauma—Research—Evaluation. 3. Adult child sexual abuse victims—Mental health—Research—Evaluation. I. Title.
RC455.4.R43P67 1997
616.85'8369—dc21
                                        97-9022
                                          CIP

Lana P. Colby, Managing Editor

Michelle McCulloch, Typography and cover design

TABLE OF CONTENTS

ACKNOWLEDGMENTS

OVER THE LAST FEW years, I have grown increasingly concerned as I have seen more and more studies of "repressed memory" and childhood sexual abuse presented to the public without any acknowledgment of the studies' often severe methodological flaws. Finally, I decided to write a few essays to alert people to the fallacies in these studies. Dr. Pamela Freyd kindly agreed to publish these on a monthly basis as columns in the False Memory Syndrome Foundation Newsletter. Writing these essays became one of my favorite activities; more pressing projects were postponed so that the monthly piece could be written. Soon, I found myself with enough ideas to fill a year's worth of Newsletters, and I decided to gather them all to create this book. Therefore, I want to thank Dr. Freyd particularly for initially offering to publish the first pieces in this series, and now for giving me permission to adapt most of the previously published columns as chapters in the present volume.

I am also indebted to many of my colleagues for their help in constructing these essays. Most of all, I thank my longstanding research partner, Dr. Jim Hudson, for his pivotal contributions. In many a long walk or dinner table conversation, Jim and I mutually worked through the logic of the arguments presented here. Jim's expertise in epidemiology, gleaned from his doctoral studies at the Harvard School of Public Health, has helped to throw into sharp focus many of the methodological flaws in the studies that I have examined. Finally, Jim's creative mind is responsible for several of the most colorful analogies that I have used in these pages. Dr. Alec Bodkin, another member of the Biological Psychiatry Laboratory, also contributed insights, especially through his collaboration in our study examining memory in survivors of the Great Barrington tornado. Paul Oliva, our research assistant, has painstakingly collected and organized for us what must be one of the best collections of scientific literature on trauma and memory anywhere. Whether recruiting tornado survivors for interviews or wading through the prose of James Fenimore Cooper, Paul has helped with this work in ways too numerous to count.

For the material in the "literature" chapter (the Children of Wish-Ton-Wish, Chapter 2), I am especially grateful to Drs. Michael Parker and Robert Madison, together with all of the members of the English Department at the United States Naval Academy, for help in searching for instances of "repression" in Western literature. Dr. Denise Spellberg and her colleagues performed a similar service for the Islamic literature.

I thank also the many people who commented on the manuscript from the perspective of their various disciplines, including Drs. Margaret Hagen, Pamela Freyd, Barry Beyerstein, Allen Feld, and Frederick Crews, together with three generations of Popes— my father, Graham; my wife, Mary; and my oldest daughter, Kimberly.

Finally, I am greatly indebted to my secretary, Fran Nestor, who miraculously found time to work on this manuscript while dealing with innumerable competing demands.

INTRODUCTION

E VERY DAY, WE READ in the newspapers, or hear on radio or television, about the findings of new scientific studies. Often these studies have direct implications for our daily lives. Various foods are reported to benefit health; environmental exposures are linked to cancer; new medications are claimed to reduce cholesterol. But few people have time to read such studies in their original form, and even fewer—including most of those in the media—have sufficient scientific training to judge the quality of the studies' methodology. Should the findings of a given study be accepted at face value? Are the data correctly interpreted? How much do we really know?

In some areas, these questions may seem unimportant. For example, when we hear of new discoveries of subatomic particles or advances in astrophysics, our lives are little affected, and most of us are content to admit scientific ignorance. But studies of psychology are different. Psychological findings may have direct implications for our beliefs about ourselves and our relationships with others. And unlike astrophysics, psychology is an area where many people harbor definite beliefs about the issues. These beliefs can sometimes be hazardous because, as an ancestor of mine originally remarked, "a little learning is a dang'rous thing." Many people, for instance, assume that it is well established that psychiatric disorders are caused by adverse childhood experiences, dysfunctional families, or stressful life events. But are they? How much does science really know about these things? How can the average person separate solid scientific findings from mere popular beliefs?

Fortunately, in the fields of psychology and psychiatry, good science has steadily expanded in the last few decades. Peer-reviewed scientific journals increasingly insist on rigorous methodology. Individual case reports have been replaced by systematic cohort studies, and speculation by statistical analysis. Not only do we know more in these fields than we did 20 years ago, but we can more readily delineate what we do not know, and what types of studies we need to do.

This book selects two areas in psychology where many people seem to think that we already know the answers, but where in fact we do not. In the first section, we suggest that there is not enough scientific evidence to support the hypothesis that it is possible to "repress" a memory—that is, to experience a terrible traumatic event and then block the memory from consciousness. The second section examines the hypothesis that childhood sexual abuse can cause individuals to develop psychiatric disorders in adulthood. Again we find that there is insufficient evidence to assess whether this hypothesis is true. We are not concluding that either of these widely held beliefs is necessarily wrong. It is just premature to say that they are right.

These assertions may shock some readers. Doesn't everybody "know" that traumatic memories can be repressed, or that childhood sexual abuse can cause adult psychiatric disorders? Are there not abundant scientific studies that have proved these hypotheses?

Of course there are many such studies, and we are not implying that these studies lack merit. Most of the studies described in this book—including even those that we criticize in detail—are careful efforts by responsible scientists. Sometimes, however, these studies are subject to unavoidable methodological limitations. Various types of bias may have influenced the findings. At other times, the findings themselves may be sound, but the conclusions drawn from the findings extend far beyond what logically can be said. Gradually, as the results of a study filter down from the original data analysis and into the hands of the public, unsupported assertions creep in. Popular books, magazine articles, and broadcast media, through mere repetition, give these claims the appearance of "fact," and many readers accept these "facts" without questioning them.

The 19 essays in this book attempt to counter this trend. In general, each essay begins by presenting a particular scientific study or group of studies, and then tries to evaluate their methodology in terms understandable to the lay reader. Methodological flaws, such as selection bias, response bias, and failure to consider confounding variables, are not hard to understand, especially when translated into more familiar examples from daily life. Thus, we make extensive use of analogies. If there is a common message to these parables, it is that even the best of modern psychological studies are still vulnerable to the old methodological difficulties that have always afflicted such research. Only by appreciating these limitations can the reader make a rigorous assessment of what psychology does and does not know.

PART ONE:
CAN INDIVIDUALS "REPRESS" MEMORIES OF TRAUMATIC EVENTS?

1

REPRESSION BY ANY OTHER NAME

THE LAST TEN YEARS have seen a flurry of interest, both in the scientific community and in the popular press, about the issue of "repressed memory." We read in magazines about abnormalities of brain anatomy and function in victims of childhood sexual abuse and other traumas. Bestselling popular books have appeared, suggesting that many adults with psychological symptoms may be the unsuspecting victims of incest or other childhood traumas of which they have no conscious memory. Sensational court cases are described in the newspapers, where plaintiffs claim to have recovered long-buried memories of horrifying sexual abuse, gruesome satanic rituals, or similar crimes suffered as children. And of course we all hear fictional accounts—in novels, television dramas, and in the movies—of people who have recovered repressed memories of terrifying childhood experiences.

But is it scientifically proven that "repression" can actually happen? Is the human brain capable of expelling the memory of a traumatic event from consciousness, and then perhaps recovering the memory years or decades later? This question has become the subject of a heated debate—a debate that history someday may record as a watershed in the evolution of scientific thought in psychology. Much hangs on the outcome of this debate. Major psychological theories, techniques for treating people suffering from psychiatric symptoms, and even important legal doctrines (such as the interpretation of "statutes of limitation") stand or fall on the outcome. Indeed, Sigmund Freud himself once wrote that repression was "the corner-stone on which the whole structure of psycho-analysis rests" (1).

In the next ten chapters, we examine the scientific evidence behind the concept of "repression." Is the "cornerstone" made of granite—confirmed by a tradition of solid scientific evidence—or is it made of sand? But before launching into this debate, we must address the question of terminology.

Many different words or phrases have been used to describe the concept that someone could develop complete amnesia for a seemingly unforgettable traumatic event. There is the standard Freudian term of "repression," which suggests that the memory of the trauma is somehow buried down in the unconscious mind, so that the individual no longer has conscious access to it. An alternative mechanism for forgetting trauma is "dissociation," first discussed in detail by the famous French psychiatrist Pierre Janet (2). Janet theorized that under conditions of severe trauma, the mind could go into a kind of trance, so that the traumatic events were not being recorded into memory in the normal way. Thus, even minutes after the traumatic event had occurred, the individual might be unaware that it had happened. But the memory would still be stored somewhere, encoded in the brain in a different manner, and still capable of breeding posttraumatic symptoms, even though the victim lacked conscious access to it. More recently, in the diagnostic manual of mental disorders published by the American Psychiatric

Association, known in the field as "DSM-IV," the term, "dissociative amnesia," is offered to describe the same hypothesized phenomenon (3). Other authorities have used the more general term "psychogenic amnesia" to refer to any sort of amnesia for a traumatic event believed to have been caused by some psychological process (4). Occasionally one hears the term "traumatic amnesia." But this phrase is somewhat more confusing, because it is also used by neurologists to describe the amnesia that can occur as a result of a head injury in which one is knocked unconscious (5).

"Repressed" or "dissociated" memories of trauma are generally considered to be very different from memories that are simply forgotten. According to most theorists, they are harbored somewhere in the mind, inaccessible to consciousness, but still capable of spawning "neurotic" symptoms, or—in more modern terminology—symptoms such as those of "posttraumatic stress disorder." Some authorities have suggested that the very fact that a memory is "repressed" contributes to psychiatric symptoms later. Under this theory, it follows that the victim must "recover" the "repressed" or "dissociated" memories and "work through" the original traumatic experience to be liberated from its aftereffects (6). In any event, terms such as "repression," "dissociation," and "psychogenic amnesia" imply a process far more profound, and usually more malignant, than the ordinary human tendency to avoid thinking about unpleasant things.

One can discuss in detail these various terms, the underlying brain mechanisms that they might suggest, and their implications for psychopathology or therapeutic intervention. But for the purposes of our discussion in the following chapters, the choice of term is irrelevant. We are not speculating here on what particular "intrapsychic" processes (i.e., changes in the inner workings of the mind) might occur at the moment of a traumatic event; we are simply asking whether it is possible for someone to develop complete amnesia for a traumatic event in the first place. In other words, we are thinking of the brain, for the purposes of discussion, as a "black box" with an input (a traumatic event, such as childhood sexual abuse) and an output (memories). If, upon examining the evidence, we find that the brain is capable of developing amnesia for traumatic events, then we can go on to the next step and speculate about what might actually be happening inside the "black box." But let us take the first step first.

In short, since it is not productive to digress into a discussion of proposed terminology or mechanisms, we will generally use the term "repression" throughout this book, although the term "dissociation" also appears occasionally. In other words, we are using "repression" or "repressed memory" as a shorthand to refer to the general concept that the mind can develop amnesia for traumatic events, regardless of the underlying presumed psychological mechanism. (However, when we speak of "repression," we are excluding amnesia due to a known biological mechanism, such as head injury or drug intoxication.) If the reader does not like our choice of the term "repression" and would prefer to substitute one of the other terms, such as "dissociation" or "psychogenic amnesia" as we go along, that is fine. It is important that we focus on the basic scientific question, without being distracted by semantics or other tangential considerations.

REFERENCES

1. Freud S. The Standard Edition of the Complete Psychological Works of Sigmund Freud. Translated and edited by Strachey J. 24 vols. London: Hogarth Press, 1953-1974. See Vol.14, p.16.

2. Janet P. L'automatisme Psychologique. Paris: Félix Alcan, 1889. A more recent discussion appears in: van der Kolk BA, Fisler R. Dissociation and the fragmentary nature of traumatic memories: Overview and explora-

tory study. J Traumatic Stress 8:505-525, 1996.

3. American Psychiatric Association. Diagnostic and Statistical Manual of Mental Disorders. 4th ed. (DSM-IV). Washington, DC: American Psychiatric Association, 1994. See p. 478.

4. See for example: Siegel DJ. Memory, trauma, and psychotherapy: A cognitive science view. J Psychotherapy Practice Research 4:93-122, 1995.

5. For examples of neurological studies on the concept of traumatic amnesia, see: Stracciari A, Ghidoni E, Guarino M, Poletti M, Pazzaglia P. Post-traumatic retrograde amnesia with selective impairment of autobiographical memory. Cortex 30:459-468,1994; or Wilson JT, Teasdale GM, Hadley DM, Wiedmann KD, Lang D. Post-traumatic amnesia: Still a valuable yardstick. J Neurol Neurosurg Psychiatry 57:198-201,1994.

6. For a detailed discussion of this theory, see for example: Herman J. Trauma and Recovery. New York: Basic Books, 1992.

2

THE CHILDREN OF
WISH-TON-WISH

To SOME PEOPLE, it seems perfectly natural that memories can be "repressed." If one experiences a tragedy too terrible to contemplate, is it not only reasonable that the mind would try to expel the memory from consciousness?

Actually, from a Darwinian point of view, repression is anything but reasonable. If, for example, one did not vividly remember being attacked by a lion, but instead repressed the memory, then one would be liable to wander in front of other lions in the future—with inauspicious consequences both for one's own survival and that of one's species. Surely it would seem more logical that Mother Nature would have designed us to remember traumatic events vividly, so that we could avoid a repetition of them in the future. And for most of us, this has been our personal experience: horrible things that have happened to us are still ingrained in our minds years after they occurred.

In a recent study, for example, members of our research group interviewed 53 victims of a freak tornado which struck the town of

Great Barrington, Massachusetts, in the Spring of 1995. One woman was trapped in her car when the storm hit; a tree fell across the road immediately in front of her, and live power lines collapsed onto the pavement behind. The car shook; the walls of a neighboring garage blew away like playing cards. In the back seat, her children were screaming.

"Did you have any loss of memory for that experience?" we asked.

She looked at us in disbelief and said, "Are you kidding?"

As this woman and many others can attest, terrifying experiences leave indelible memories. Therefore, where and when did the idea arise that the opposite could happen—that a traumatic memory could be completely banished from consciousness?

One way to examine this question is to look at world literature. If repression were a real phenomenon, experienced by human beings across the ages, we might reasonably expect to see it regularly in stories, poems, and dramas written throughout history. If we inspect the literature of different eras and different cultures, where do we find characters who repressed and then perhaps later recovered memories of traumatic events?

We have put this question to a number of literary experts. Such a survey, admittedly, is hardly a formal scientific study, but it is nevertheless revealing. Throughout most of history, it appears, no one in any story in the world's literature appears to have developed amnesia for a seemingly unforgettable traumatic event and later recovered that memory into consciousness. No one in the Bible, for example, seems to have repressed and then recovered a memory. Nor in Shakespeare—a veritable catalog of the possible permutations of the human psyche—do we find a clear instance of repression. No one has been able to show us a clear case of repression in classical Greek or Roman literature, in Islamic literature, or anywhere else in Western literature until the 19th century. Then, and only then, does repression begin to crop up (1).

As best as we can tell, one of the first cases of repression and recovery of memory appears in James Fenimore Cooper's 1829 novel, *The Wept of Wish-Ton-Wish* (2). In this tale, set in the mid-seventeenth century, Indians attack the little settlement of Wish-Ton-Wish in Connecticut and abduct two children. One is a teenager named Whittal Ring, and the other is a little girl named Ruth Heathcote. Years later, Rueben Ring comes upon his lost brother Whittal in the woods. Whittal is now dressed as an Indian; he is wearing war paint and calls himself Nipset. He has complete amnesia for his past as a White man. His sister, Faith, recognizes her brother, but is unable to persuade him of his former identity, even when she shows him his own white skin.

Later, Ruth is also found. She, too, has become an Indian and goes by the name of Narra-mattah. Her memories of childhood are also repressed, but she has recurring images of her mother in dreams:

Narra-mattah has forgotten all . . . But she sees one that the wives of the Narragansetts do not see. She sees a woman with white skin; her eyes look softly on her child . . .

Ruth's mother tries to help her child recover her lost memories, but in vain. Then, at the very end of the novel, the child falls ill and lies dying. And there, in the lush romantic prose of Cooper, we witness what just might be literature's first case of recovery of a repressed memory. Ruth's mother (who is also named Ruth) speaks to her:

"Look on thy friends, long-mourned and much suffering daughter! 'Tis she who sorrowed over thy infant afflictions, who rejoiced in thy childish happiness, and who hath so bitterly wept thy loss, that craveth the boon. In this awful moment, recall the lessons of youth.

Surely, surely, the God that bestowed thee in mercy, though he hath led thee on a wonderful and inscrutable path, will not desert thee at the end! Think of thy early instruction, child of my love; feeble of spirit as thou art, the seed may yet quicken, though it hath been cast where the glory of the promise hath so long been hid."

"Mother!" said a low struggling voice in reply. The word reached every ear, and it caused a general and breathless attention. The sound was soft and low, perhaps infantile, but it was uttered without accent, and clearly.

"Mother—why are we in the forest?" continued the speaker. "Have any robbed us of our home, that we dwell beneath the trees?"

Ruth raised a hand imploringly, for none to interrupt the illusion.

"Nature hath revived the recollections of her youth," she whispered. "Let the spirit depart, if such be his holy will, in the blessedness of infant innocence!"

Another possible case of repression arises in 1859, in Charles Dickens' novel, *A Tale of Two Cities* (3). Dr. Manette, after 18 years imprisonment in the Bastille, has developed amnesia for long intervals of his past, including the period surrounding his release. He describes his amnesia in courtroom testimony:

"Has it been your misfortune to undergo a long imprisonment, without trial, or even accusation, in your native country, Doctor Manette?"

He answered in a tone that went to every heart, "A long imprisonment."

"Were you newly released on the occasion in question?"

"They tell me so."

"Have you no remembrance of the occasion?"

"None. My mind is a blank, for some time—I cannot even say

what time—when I employed myself, in my captivity, in making shoes, to the time when I found myself living in London with my dear daughter here. She had become familiar to me, when a gracious God restored my faculties; but, I am unable even to say how she had become familiar. I have no remembrance of the process."

And a few years later, in approximately 1862, Emily Dickinson implies more specifically that an event could breed amnesia simply because it is too traumatic to contemplate (4):

> *There is a pain—so utter -*
> *It swallows substance up -*
> *Then covers the Abyss with Trance -*
> *So Memory can step*
> *Around—across—upon it -*
> *As one within a Swoon -*
> *Goes safely —where an open eye -*
> *Would drop Him—Bone by Bone.*

By the end of the century, we find that repression and recovery of memory have entered romantic fiction in full-blown form. A typical case appears in the 1896 children's novel, *Captains Courageous*, by a Nobel prize winner, Rudyard Kipling (5). One of the characters in the novel is a former preacher, Penn, who lost his entire family years earlier in a tragic flood. After the flood, Penn has completely repressed the memory of the entire trauma, and has even forgotten that he ever was a preacher or had a family. We find him instead working for Captain Disko Troop as a fisherman on a Grand Banks schooner, oblivious to his past. One day, a passing ocean liner carves a neighboring fishing schooner in two, killing its hands, including the captain's son. The surviving captain is rescued by Disko's crew and brought aboard. At this moment, Penn abruptly undergoes a trans-formation. He suddenly recovers the memory of the loss of his own family, and his voice transforms from his usual "pitiful little titter" to the authoritative tones of a preacher. He consoles the grieving captain, prays for him, and shares with him the memory of the tragic loss of his own loved ones years ago. And then, within hours, Penn "re-represses" the memory. He again forgets his past, reverts to a simple fisherman, and asks for his custom-ary game of checkers.

With the coming of modern times, repression has found a new and even more fertile soil in that uniquely 20th century art form, film. From the thrillers of Alfred Hitchcock to the childhood trauma of Batman, characters in the movies regularly experience amnesia for traumatic events, and then, at some dramatic moment, recover the memory. Indeed, repression is the perfect device for Hollywood. Many a celluloid hero is seen having a "flashback"—a fleeting, freeze-frame image, perhaps slightly out of focus—of a long for-gotten event. What is the dark secret from the past? Perhaps, if the hero could make sense of this recurring image, recover the repressed memory, all would be explained. By the end of the movie, this is usually just what has happened.

In short, for all of us who have grown up in the 20th century, repression seems like a natural phenomenon. We have read of it in novels and seen it in the movies all our lives. Perhaps this is why so many people accept the concept without bothering to question it. But we must stop to remember that repression actually appears to be a parochial notion, seemingly restricted only to recent times and only to Western culture. And we must also remember that repres-sion was not a scientific hypothesis first proposed by Sigmund Freud or Pierre Janet. Rather, it seems to have arisen as a romantic notion in the Victorian era, somewhere in the middle of the 19th century. It had entered poetry and prose well before Freud and Janet were even born. It has continued to flourish in literature and cinema throughout the 20th century. It is a powerful dramatic device that makes for good fiction.

But does it make for good science? We explore this question in the following chapters.

REFERENCES

1. The notion of repression also began to evolve in the writings of 19th century philosophers such as Schopenhauer and Nietzsche. For a detailed discussion of these beginnings, see: Ellenberger H. The Discovery of the Unconscious. New York: Basic Books, 1970.

2. Cooper JF. (1829) The Wept of Wish-Ton-Wish. New York: Appleton and Co., 1901.

3. Dickens C. (1859) A Tale of Two Cities. New York: Dodd, Mead & Co., 1942. See Book the Second, Chapter 3.

4. Johnson TH, ed. The Complete Poems of Emily Dickinson. Boston: Little, Brown & Co., 1960. See p. 294, Poem no. 599. I am indebted to Dr. Gail S. Goodman and her colleagues for having discovered this poem. See: Goodman GS, Quas JA, Batterman-Faunce JM, Riddlesberger MM, Kuhn J. Predictors of accurate and inaccurate memories of traumatic events experienced in childhood. Consciousness Cognition 4:269-274, 1994.

5. Kipling R. (1896) Captains Courageous: A Story of the Grand Banks. New York: Doubleday, Page & Co., 1925. See Chapters 3 and 7.

3

THE EMPEROR'S TAILORING

MODERN TECHNOLOGY has greatly expanded our ability to study the structure and functions of the brain. Neuropsychological testing techniques, measurements of neurotransmitters (chemical messengers), and other advances in the understanding of brain chemistry have allowed us to probe ever deeper into the central nervous system. Perhaps the most dazzling technological strides have occurred in neuroimaging: with magnetic resonance imaging (MRI) and positron emission tomography (PET), we can now see images of living brain structures. With the appropriate computer software, we can detect subtle differences in anatomy or blood flow between different brain regions, or between patient populations and normal comparison subjects. Can we apply this technological arsenal to answer the question of whether it is possible to repress the memory of traumatic events?

At first, the answer to this question would seem to be yes. The literature has recently become filled with studies using various forms of high technology to study trauma and its consequences (1). For example, neuropsychological testing techniques have been used to quantify memory function in trauma victims as compared to nontraumatized comparison subjects. These studies have usually found that individuals diagnosed with posttraumatic stress disorder (PTSD) have greater difficulty remembering test items than do normal comparison subjects. Biochemical studies, similarly, have shown that numerous chemicals critical to the function of the nervous system, such as neuropeptides and neurotransmitters, may be affected by stress. Among the chemicals studied in this manner are epinephrine; norepinephrine; corticosteroids; pituitary and hypothalamic hormones that stimulate the release of corticosteroids; opioid peptides; gamma-aminobutyric acid; vasopressin; and many others. Not surprisingly, data suggest that these substances are disrupted in various ways during the experience of trauma. They may even remain disrupted long afterwards in trauma survivors with PTSD. Furthermore, other studies have shown that many of these same neuropeptides and neurotransmitters have various effects on memory function, either enhancing or impairing memory under particular conditions.

Even more striking, however, are the latest studies of brain anatomy and metabolism in trauma victims. For example, studies of monkeys exposed to prolonged and fatal stress have shown damage in an area of the brain called the hippocampus (2). And damage to the hippocampus, in turn, has been shown to be associated with impairments in memory function. MRI studies of the hippocampus in humans diagnosed with PTSD have now also shown abnormalities in comparisons with healthy control subjects. (We discuss this particular finding in greater detail in Chapter 18.) Even more impressive are the findings of PET scans in trauma victims. For example, PET technology has been used to measure cerebral glucose metabolism (an index of brain activity) in combat veterans as compared to normal controls. Differences between the two groups were found in a number of different cortical areas (3). In another study, 8 patients with posttraumatic stress disorder, 2 of whom were victims of childhood sexual abuse, were exposed to "traumatic" versus "neutral" scripts while undergoing positron emission tomography (4). In the traumatic scripts, audiotapes describing a personal traumatic experience, such as sexual abuse or a car accident, were played to the subject. The neutral scripts were audiotapes describing mundane experiences, such as emptying the dishwasher. Statistical mapping techniques were then applied to the PET scan results to identify which areas of the brain's cortex displayed significant activation under the different conditions. The 8 subjects with PTSD were specifically selected for the study because they had already been shown to demonstrate a physiologic response (in other words, measurable physical changes) in response to traumatic scripts. Therefore, it is probably not surprising that, when stimulated to remember their trauma, the subjects' brains showed changes; there were significant differences in blood flow in various parts of their brains when they were thinking about watching their loved ones die in a car accident as opposed to, say, thinking about brushing their teeth. Upon comparing the color-enhanced computer printouts of the PET scans, even a lay person can see obvious differences in the pictures taken in the traumatic condition versus the neutral condition.

These are all interesting and valuable studies, carefully performed under rigorous scientific conditions. What's more, some have produced dramatic findings. One can hardly examine the striking PET scan images without being impressed. Surely, then, this wealth of data provides mounting evidence that trauma does influence memory, and suggests neurological and biochemical mechanisms that might explain how trauma victims could develop amnesia for the event. One might believe, therefore, that we are finally accumulating scientific proof that memories of trauma can be repressed.

But this last conclusion is a fallacy, and it is important to understand why. The logical flaw here is the assumption that a phenomenon is demonstrated just because inferences from various studies can be linked together to suggest a mechanism whereby that phenomenon might occur. An example will make this clear. Studies have established that there is a highly significant positive correlation, throughout the animal kingdom, between brain size and intelligence. In other words, the larger the brain, the more flexible and adaptive is the behavior of the species. In this sense, worms are not as intelligent as seagulls, and seagulls are not as intelligent as dogs. It has also been established, through years of neuroanatomical studies, that men have bigger brains, on average, than women. But even though these two findings are both correct, it would be erroneous to infer that men have higher IQ's than women. If we are interested in knowing whether men are smarter than women, we should stop drawing dangerous inferences from neuroanatomy, and instead go out and test actual samples of men and women for intelligence. By analogy, if one wishes to test whether trauma victims can repress their memories, one should go out and simply ask a group of victims if they can remember their trauma (as we will discuss in greater detail in subsequent chapters). If instead we merely infer that repression might occur on the basis of people's cerebral glucose metabolism, or images of their hippocampi, we might prove seriously mistaken.

This fallacy may seem obvious, but it has bedeviled even the most brilliant thinkers. For example, the great Austrian mathematician Kurt Gödel once performed a series of mathematical calculations based on Einstein's equations from his theory of relativity (5). Gödel's calculations suggested that certain solutions to Einstein's equations produced closed time lines, which would theoretically allow for the existence of time travel. Unfortunately, Gödel found that the amount of energy necessary for a human being to travel back in time would be excessively large. He apparently believed, however, that his calculations did offer a possible mechanism for the existence of ghosts.

Even the best of scientific findings, in other words, can be misused to reach dubious conclusions. And the average observer, blinded by the technological sophistication of such findings, may lose track of the sleight-of-hand inferences that someone is making from them. Such fallacious reasoning has often infiltrated the courtroom, where juries may be presented with impressive scientific results, strung together to reach dubious conclusions: that working at video display terminals can cause miscarriages, that the drug Bendectin can cause birth defects, that silicone breast implants can cause arthritic disease, or that low-intensity magnetic fields can cause cancer (6,7). The point, once again, is that if one wants to test these hypotheses, one should not dwell on inferences from laboratory studies. One should simply go out in Nature and test whether the hypotheses are true.

One last example of this fallacy, taken directly from modern psychology, surrounds the technique of "eye movement desensitization and reprocessing," usually abbreviated as "EMDR." EMDR is a novel psychotherapeutic technique in which the patient is asked to follow a moving object with his or her eyes while thinking about a traumatic experience (8). On the basis of a series of inferences from various scientific findings, proponents of EMDR claim that it is effective for the treatment of a range of psychiatric disorders. The reasoning goes something like this: it is well established that during one stage of sleep, called rapid-eye-movement sleep, or REM sleep, the eyes move rapidly back and forth. It is also known that REM sleep is associated with dreaming. Dreaming, in turn, is often associated with intense emotions. And trauma victims, indisputably, may have dreams about the trauma that they have experienced. Therefore, if a patient voluntarily engages in eye movements in the therapist's office, while recalling a traumatic experience, perhaps he or she could more effectively reexperience and "work through" the traumatic experience, with consequent progress in therapy.

An interesting chain of speculations and extrapolations, perhaps, and one that is indeed based on legitimate scientific observations. But to start with, just because trauma causes bad dreams, why should we assume that simulating a dream state will undo the effects of trauma? This is comparable to reasoning that because rainy days cause us to take out our umbrellas, then taking out our umbrellas on a sunny day will produce rain.

Furthermore, the fact remains that no one has clearly shown, in a methodologically sound study, that EMDR actually works. That is, when we put inferences aside and go out to actually test the efficacy of EMDR in nature, using a properly placebo-controlled design, the hypothesis is not supported (9).

What is the lesson of all of this? It is that a phenomenon is not proven just because findings from various studies can be combined to suggest a mechanism for how the phenomenon might theoretically occur. In other words, no matter how impressive the findings of neurotransmitter assays or how colorful the pictures from PET scans, and no matter how intriguing the brain mechanisms that these studies might suggest, we cannot logically conclude from these studies that people can actually repress memories of traumatic events.

In other words, we should not speculate about the details of the emperor's tailoring until we have first checked to see whether he has any clothes.

REFERENCES

1. For a review, see: Bremner JD, Krystal JH, Charney DS, Southwick SM. Neural mechanisms in dissociative amnesia for childhood abuse: Relevance to the current controversy surrounding the "false memory syndrome." Am J Psychiatry 153:71-82, 1996.

2. Uno H, Tarara R, Else JG, Suleman MA, Sapolsky RM. Hippocampal damage associated with prolonged and fatal stress in primates. J Neurosci 9:1705-1711,1989.

3. Bremner JD, Ng CK, Staib L, Markey J, Duncan KJ, Zubal G, et al. PET measurement of cerebral metabolism following a noradrenergic challenge in patients with post-traumatic stress disorder and in healthy subjects. (abstract) J Nucl Med 34:205P-206P, 1993.

4. Rauch SL, van der Kolk BA, Fisler RE, Alpert NM, Orr SP, Savage CR, et al. A symptom provocation study of posttraumatic stress disorder using positron emission tomography and script-driven imagery. Arch Gen Psychiatry 53:380-387,1996.

5. Stillwell J. Mathematics and its History. New York: Springer -Verlag, 1989. See pp. 330-331.

6. Foster KR, Bernstein DE, Huber PW, eds. Phantom Risk. Cambridge: MIT Press, 1993. For the classic original discussion of "junk science" in legal testimony, see also: Huber PW. Galileo's Revenge: Junk Science in the Courtroom. New York: Basic Books, 1991.

7. Angell M. Shattuck Lecture—Evaluating the health risks of breast implants: The interplay of medical science, the law, and public opinion. New Engl J Med 334:1513-1518, 1996.

8. Hudson JI, Chase EA, Pope HG Jr. Eye movement densitization and reprocessing in eating disorders: Caution against premature acceptance. Int J Eating Disorders. In press.

9. Admittedly, there are some studies which claim to show a benefit for EMDR. These include, for example: Silver SM, Brooks A, Obenchain J. Treatment of Vietnam War veterans with PTSD: A comparison of eye movement desensitization and reprocessing, biofeedback, and relaxation training. J Traumatic Stress 8:337-343,1996; and Montgomery R, Ayllon T. Eye movement desensitization across subjects: Subjective and physiological measures of treatment efficacy. J Behavior Therapy Exp Psychiatry 25:217-230,1994. However, in our opinion even these studies are subject to methodological flaws, which make their findings highly questionable. For a discussion of these flaws, see the review in note 8, above, and also: Steketee G, Goldstein A. Reflections on Shapiro's reflections: Testing EMDR within a theoretical context. The Beh Therapist 17:156-157, 1994, or any of several other critical reviews cited by Hudson and colleagues in their review above.

4

THE SICKLE CELL VICTIMS

LITTLE IS TO BE gained, as seen in the previous chapter, if we attempt to prove or disprove the theory of repression by performing biological studies of the brain. We must go out and study actual victims of trauma to see what happens in real life. But here, the experience of real life would at first seem to argue against the possibility of repression, in that we remember traumatic events much better than trivial ones. We remember a car accident months or years after it occurred, but we have long forgotten what we had for breakfast on the morning of the car accident.

In fact, research has specifically suggested that emotional arousal improves our ability to remember events. In one recent study, a group of investigators gave two short stories to experimental subjects (1). In the "neutral version," a boy has an uneventful day during which he witnesses a hospital disaster drill. In the "arousal version," the boy is hit by a car in a terrible accident and rushed to the hospital with life-threatening injuries. Before presenting these stories, the investigators gave their subjects a drug called propranolol. This drug, in simple terms, reduces the physical symptoms of emotional arousal. The propranolol had no effect on the subjects' ability to remember the neutral story, but it impaired their memory of the arousing story. These findings suggest that one's memory is better under conditions of full emotional arousal than under conditions where this arousal has been blunted by medication. Since trauma is arousing, therefore, it should be expected to enhance rather than inhibit memory.

However, if one is searching for evidence of repression, perhaps car accidents are the wrong place to look. For example, one prominent theorist, Dr. Lenore Terr, has speculated that individuals rarely forget single episodes of trauma like a car accident (she calls these single episodes "type I" traumas), but can develop amnesia for repeated episodes of trauma (which she calls "type II" traumas) (2). This theory would seem counter to intuition; most of us would agree that the more often something is repeated, the better we remember it. At least one experimental study supports this intuition: children subjected to repeated medical procedures remember the events better than children subjected to only a single procedure (3). Nevertheless, Terr argues that an individual subjected to a single unexpected trauma might possess no innate ability to banish the memory from consciousness, whereas someone experiencing the same trauma over and over again might gradually "learn" to dissociate—to go into a sort of trance—at the time that the trauma was happening. Eventually, the victim might become skilled at developing amnesia for intolerable experiences. For example, a child subjected to repeated experiences of sexual abuse might gradually learn to imagine herself in a field of flowers, far away from her actual body, during the time that the abuse was occurring. Thus she could display amnesia for the trauma even moments after it occurred.

If one believes that this could occur, then it is only one more step to believe in the possibility of what has been called "robust repression"—the idea that one could develop amnesia not just for a few events, but for a massive dose of prolonged and repeated trauma (4). Some authorities are convinced that this is possible, perhaps even common (5). But is the human mind really capable of doing this? Could people become so good at dissociating that they could, in effect, erase the memories of hundreds of individual episodes of trauma, extending over months or years of time?

One response to this question comes from a very interesting investigation, in which a group of experts on hypnosis located a group of victims with recurrent traumatic episodes of pain, and actually attempted to train them to dissociate! In this study, Dr. David Dinges and a large group of collaborators treated 78 patients, most of them boys and young adults, with sickle cell anemia (6). Sickle cell anemia is the most common serious genetic disease afflicting African-Americans. It is characterized by periodic, unpredictable, painful "crises" which occur when blood vessels become occluded by clumps of abnormal sickle-shaped red blood cells. Incapacitating crises can occur at any time—in the middle of a young child's birthday party, while playing in the back yard, or while out on a date. Certainly, if one could learn to dissociate at the time of such a trauma, it would be a great advantage.

The patients were enrolled for up to one year. For 5 to 7 months, they were administered weekly group training sessions to learn self-hypnosis. Thereafter they received biweekly sessions for another 6 months. In a preliminary analysis of the first 37 patients to complete the study, some promising results were observed: the number of days with pain was reduced by 8% and the number of days that subjects required pain medication was reduced by 6%. However, the crises experienced during the self-hypnosis treatment actually lasted longer, and were rated as more intense by the patients themselves. Overall, it appeared that self-hypnosis reduced the milder episodes of pain, but did not affect the more severe episodes. There was no evidence that any of the subjects could learn to forget their painful crises.

Now, it of course might be argued that crises of physical pain differ from the trauma of repeated physical or sexual abuse. However, we cannot ignore the findings of the sickle cell study: even with intensive training by experts, people can learn to "dissociate" only to a modest degree, and cannot obliterate major traumatic events from their memories. Thus, it would seem unlikely that a child, lacking any training in self-hypnosis at all, could become so adept at dissociating that he or she could completely expel an entire series of abuse experiences from consciousness. At the least, then, if one claims that individuals can develop amnesia for episodes of sexual abuse via "dissociation" or another such mechanism, one would be obliged to demonstrate how victims of sexual abuse have a unique ability to do this, when victims of sickle cell anemia, even after a year of professional training in self-hypnosis, cannot.

REFERENCES

1.   Cahill L, Prins B, Weber M, McGaugh JL. ß-adrenergic activation and memory for emotional events. Nature 371:702-704, 1994.

2.   Terr LC. Childhood traumas: An outline and overview. Am J Psychiatry 148:10-20, 1991.

3.   Goodman GS, Quas JA, Batterman-Faunce JM, Riddlesberger MM, Kuhn J. Predictors of accurate and inaccurate memories of traumatic events experienced in childhood. Consciousness Cognition 4:269-274, 1994.

4.   For a detailed criticism of the concept of "robust repression," see: Ofshe RJ, Singer MT. Recovered-memory therapy and robust repression: Influence and pseudomemories. Int J Clin Exp Hypn 42:391-410, 1994; or the popular book: Ofshe RJ, Waters E. Making Monsters: False Memories, Psychotherapy and Sexual Hysteria. New York: Scribners, 1994.

5. For works espousing the possibility of "robust repression," see the references cited under "The Opposing Position" in the Further Reading section at the back of this book.

6. Dinges DF, Orne EC, Bloom PB, Ohene-Frempong K, Dampier C, Shapiro BS, et al. Medical self-hypnosis in the adjunctive management of organic pain: A prospective study of sickle cell pain. (abstract) Presented at the NIH Workshop on Biobehavioral Pain Research, Rockville, MD, January 19, 1994.

5

THE 86-MILE-PER-HOUR TREES

A S SUGGESTED IN THE previous chapter, some people might argue that studies of physical pain, as in the sickle cell victims, would not apply to emotional traumas, such as longstanding sexual abuse. After all, one does not read case reports of sickle cell victims who repressed the memory of their "crises." But one can find published case reports of individuals who appear to have repressed the memory of childhood sexual abuse (1). Do such case reports represent useful scientific evidence?

In answer to this question, it is productive to recall some of the other case reports that have appeared in the scientific literature from time to time. For example, a report in the prestigious *American Journal of Psychiatry* described a woman who appeared to have acquired the ability to speak another language by seemingly supernatural means (2). She was said to display a secondary personality, capable of speaking a language that she had never learned, that tended to appear on the eighth day of the waxing or waning moon. The authors did not provide any explanation based upon known scientific principles for this case of "paranormally acquired speech." Similarly, one can find compelling case reports of individuals who have had experiences in past lives (3,4) and, of course, individuals who have been abducted by space aliens (5). To most of us, these various phenomena seem inconsistent with our common sense and experience. Yet they have all been described in detailed case reports. Therefore, should we assume that such phenomena actually occur? And if not, why do we not accept these case reports as adequate evidence?

The reason that we do not is because of a principle known in science as "measurement error." This term refers to the fact that, when one makes a large number of observations, a few mistakes are bound to occur. In other words, there is a certain "background noise," due to occasional "false-positive" observations, which permeates even the most careful studies. A classic example of such a "false-positive" was obtained by a police department in Florida that used a radar gun to clock a grove of trees moving at 86 miles per hour, and a house moving at a more leisurely 20 miles per hour (6). In other words, although radar is usually accurate (as most of us unfortunately know), it is, like everything else, vulnerable to false-positive observations.

How do scientists deal with the problem of "measurement error?" There are various methods, depending upon the type of research being conducted. For example, if we know that a test for the HIV virus is wrong approximately 1% of the time, and this test yields a 10% prevalence rate for HIV in a given population of individuals, we can state with reasonable confidence (depending on the size of the population) that this population has an elevated rate of HIV infection. In other words, our finding cannot be explained merely by the rate of false positives expected from the test. This case is an example of what the United States Supreme Court had in mind, in its pivotal *Daubert* ruling, when it required that a scientific test have a "known rate of error" in order to be admissible in expert scientific testimony (7). When the rate of error is unknown, and possibly high—as in such methods as hand-writing analysis, lie detector tests, or hypnotically refreshed memory—then the admissibility of the evidence is thrown into question. It may be ruled "junk science" and thrown out of the courtroom.

Returning now to the issues of repression and recovered memory, we find an analogous situation. There are unquestionably various anecdotal cases in which individuals have provided dramatic stories of an allegedly repressed memory that was subsequently recovered years later, and where corroborating evidence was reportedly found to prove that the recovered memory was true. Some of these cases appear compelling. But then, when we consider that literally hundreds of thousands of therapists and counselors of every description have seen many millions of patients over the years, one would expect to see some published case descriptions of repressed memory, purely as a result of measurement error alone. Specifically, if the rate of "false positives" were only one in one thousand, but we have a denominator of millions of patients, one might find hundreds or thousands of "cases" even of a phenomenon which did not actually exist at all.

Now of course, diagnosing "repression" in a patient is not a mechanical technique like clocking speeds with a radar gun. But since there is no mechanical method to test the existence of repression in a given case, the rate of error is even harder to calculate. Further, since the diagnosis of repression relies on the verbal reports of the patient and the impressions of the therapist, it is much more likely to be influenced by the underlying beliefs of the two parties than would a measurement performed with a machine. Such beliefs introduce yet another degree of uncertainty into the error rate.

With repression, in other words, we have not only a large and unknown denominator, but also little idea of the rate of error to be expected. If we studied 100 patients with symptoms of posttraumatic stress disorder, and found 2 individuals with seemingly clear, corroborated cases of repressed memory, would this finding represent a satisfactory scientific demonstration of repression? Or would a 2% rate be simply the level of "background noise" to be expected from measurement error alone? If the 2% rate is due to measurement error, then the study would offer no evidence for repression at all. Because we do not know the rate of "false positives" to be expected in this situation, we would require a robust prevalence of documented cases of repression in our hypothetical study to be certain that we were comfortably above the level that could be accounted for by measurement error.

In summary, then, when we hear a dramatic and seemingly ironclad case example of some individual who appears to have repressed and recovered a memory of childhood sexual abuse or other trauma, it is easy to be impressed. Indeed, such cases may be valuable as "hypothesis-generating" evidence. In other words, they suggest that the concept of repression would be worth studying. But they provide no proof: they are not legitimate "hypothesis-testing" evidence. In the modern scientific debate on the existence of repression and recovered memory, such case reports have no more place than the 20-mile-per-hour house or the 86-mile-per-hour trees.

REFERENCES

1. See, for example: Martínez-Taboas A. Repressed memories: Some clinical data contributing towards its elucidation. Am J Psychotherapy 50:217-230, 1996; and Apitzsch H. Trauma and dissociation in refugee patients. Nord J Psychiatry 50:333-336, 1996.

2. Stevenson I, Pasricha S. A case of secondary personality with xenoglossy. Am J Psychiatry 136:1591-1592, 1979.

3. Pasricha S, Stevenson I. Three cases of the reincarnation type in India. Ind J Psychiatry 19:36-42, 1977. For a critique of Stevenson's work, which points out the danger of reporting "astounding matches" while minimizing non-matches and inconsistencies, see: Angel L. Empirical evidence for reincarnation? Examining Stevenson's "most impressive" case. The Skeptical Inquirer 18:481-487, 1994.

4. Woolger R. Other Lives, Other Selves. New York: Doubleday, 1987.

5   Mack JE. Abduction: Human Encounters with Aliens. New York: Scribners, 1994.

6. Smith D, Tomerlin J. Beating the Radar Rap. Chicago: Bonus Books, 1990.

7. Daubert v. Merrell-Dow Pharmaceuticals. U.S. Supreme Court, December 2, 1992. No. 92-102.

6

Do You Remember Whether You Forgot?

W E HAVE NOW NARROWED the field of studies that would represent acceptable evidence for repression. Biological and neuropsychological studies of the brain are not helpful, because they provide no direct test of the hypothesis. Individual case reports are also largely non-contributory because of the issue of measurement error. Therefore, we need to study entire samples of trauma victims, not just one or two individuals.

We are still left with a fair number of studies to examine. These can be divided into "retrospective" and "prospective" designs (although this terminology is only approximate). In retrospective studies, the investigators examine subjects who currently remember a traumatic event, but are believed to have repressed the memory at some time in the past. In prospective studies, the investigators follow up on the victims of a known trauma to see whether any of them have developed amnesia for it. In this chapter and the next, we examine retrospective studies that claim to show evidence for repression; in the following three chapters, we discuss prospective studies which have examined memory in victims of various types of trauma.

Among retrospective studies seeking to demonstrate repression of memories of childhood sexual abuse, most have used essentially the same design (1-8). Three particularly good examples of this design appear together in the October, 1995, issue of the *Journal of Traumatic Stress* (6-8). In these studies, the investigators examined a group of individuals who currently claimed to remember that they were victims of childhood sexual abuse or some other traumatic event. Then, the investigators asked these individuals whether there had been any period of time in the past when they had forgotten about the trauma. In each of the three studies, a certain number of the subjects reported that they had "forgotten" the traumatic event for some period of time in the past. Can we conclude that these individuals had repressed the memory of the trauma?

Such a conclusion would be premature for several reasons. Most importantly, none of the three studies provides validation for the questions asked about "forgetting." In other words, the investigators did not test whether a "yes" answer on the question actually meant that the respondent had amnesia. Instead, perhaps individuals answering "yes" simply meant that there had been a period of time when they preferred not to think about the traumatic event, or a period when they were preoccupied with other activities and simply did not bestow any thought on the event. If so, then a "yes" answer would not indicate true repression at all.

The importance of validating a question can be illustrated by example. Suppose that one did a survey of 100 people and asked them, "have you ever experienced a hallucination?" If 20 of the 100 people answered "yes," would we be justified in concluding that 20% of the population has a history of "schizophrenic symptoms?" Obviously not—we would have to show that a "yes" answer on our screening question corresponded to a genuine experience of hallucinations as they are defined in published diagnostic criteria for schizophrenia.

Another example of the importance of validation can be found in the study by Linda Meyer Williams, "Recovered memories of abuse in women with documented child sexual victimization histories" (6). In this study, Williams presents actual case histories of 5 individuals who are said to have forgotten an episode of childhood sexual abuse and to have then recovered the memory. However, when we read these case reports, we find that one of the women (case 3) stated, "Well, I guess I may not have completely forgotten about it after my mother talked to me, but blocked it out most of the time, just stopped thinking about it." With regard to another woman (case 4), Williams states, "she reported that periodically when she is happy, she forgets." These two examples hardly sound like genuine amnesia.

A second methodological problem with these studies is the question of whether the traumatic events actually occurred. In one of the studies, by Elliott and Briere (7), no corroboration is provided; in fact, the subjects were never actually seen or interviewed by the investigators, and data were obtained only from mailed-in questionnaires. In another study, by van der Kolk and Fisler (8), it is stated that many of the individuals claimed to have corroboration, but the investigators did not assess the quality of the corroboration for themselves. Only in the Williams study is it claimed that all cases were corroborated. But what is meant here by corroboration? Consider again an actual case example presented by Williams, in which a 4-year-old girl reportedly was subjected to sexual intercourse by her uncle. Studies have shown that vaginal penetration of a 4-year-old girl by an adult almost invariably leaves medical findings. For example, in one study (9), 96% of girls between the ages of 4 and 10 who experienced genito-genital contact exhibited medical findings on unaided examination. But in this girl, according to the article, no medical findings were seen, and the uncle stated that the abuse did not occur. Certainly, one would be hesitant to accept this case as "corroborated." Yet it is classified as such in the article. How many other cases in this and other studies might also be based on dubious "corroboration?"

Third, there is the problem of early childhood amnesia. A child might experience a trauma at the age of 3 or 4, and then forget it via the normal process of childhood amnesia. Then, later, the child is told about the event, and gradually comes to believe that he or she has remembered the event independently. Most of us have had this experience: our parents or other adults have told us about an event (traumatic or otherwise) that occurred in our childhood, and we gradually come to regard the memory as our own, even though we have actually reconstructed it from the accounts of others. If we subsequently report that we "forgot" and later "recovered" this memory, it would be invalid to conclude from our report that repression occurred.

In short, studies using this design—asking subjects whether they "remember whether they forgot" an event—are subject to several important methodological limitations that compromise interpretation of their results. Even if we were to see 20 more studies using this same design, we would still not be in any better position to conclude that individuals are truly capable of repressing the memory of traumatic events. Only a prospective study, in which subjects with an unequivocally documented trauma are subsequently interviewed and asked directly if they remember the event, can properly test the hypothesis that repression can occur.

References

1. Briere J, Conte J. Self-reported amnesia for abuse in adults molested as children. J Traumatic Stress 6:21-31, 1993.

2. Loftus EF, Polonsky S, Fullilove MT. Memories of childhood sexual abuse: Remembering and repressing. Psychology of Women Quarterly 18:67-84, 1994.

3. Feldman-Summers S, Pope KS. The experience of "forgetting" childhood abuse: A national survey of psychologists. J Consult Clin Psychology 62:636-639, 1994.

4. Gold SN, Hughes D, Hohnecker L. Degrees of repression of sexual abuse memories. Am Psychologist 49:441-442, 1994.

5. Roe CM, Peterson FL, Schwartz MF. Previously forgotten memories of sexual abuse: A descriptive study. Paper presented at the 10th Annual Meeting, International Society for Traumatic Stress Studies, Chicago, November 1994.

6. Williams LM. Recovered memories of abuse in women with documented child sexual victimization histories. J Traumatic Stress 8:649-673, 1995.

7. Elliot DM, Briere J. Posttraumatic stress associated with the delayed recall of sexual abuse: A general population study. J Traumatic Stress 8:629-647, 1995.

8. van der Kolk BA, Fisler R. Dissociation and the fragmentary nature of traumatic memories: Overview and exploratory study. J Traumatic Stress 8:505-525, 1995.

9. Muram D. Child sexual abuse—Genital tract findings in prepubertal girls. I: The unaided medical examination. Am J Obstet Gynecol 160:328-333, 1989.

7

DON'T FORGET YOUR JACKET!

As ILLUSTRATED IN OUR analysis of the "do-you-remember-whether-you-forgot" studies, retrospective designs are fraught with hazards, because they are only as good as the subject's ability to describe past events accurately. Such descriptions may or may not correspond to what actually happened.

Suppose, for example, that we were to design a retrospective study to test the hypothesis that forgetting to wear one's jacket can cause the common cold. We recruit 100 mothers and give them a questionnaire asking them to recall when their children developed colds during the past winter. For each cold reported, we then ask the mother whether the cold was preceded by failure to wear a jacket. We might well find a high correlation between the forgetting of jackets and the onset of colds. But would any serious scientist accept our findings? Of course not. The mothers' recollections may be biased in any number of ways—especially if many of our mothers already believe in the "jacket hypothesis" before they enter our study!

With these considerations in mind, let us examine some of the newer retrospective studies of repression. Several of these studies have described individuals who reportedly repressed and later recovered the memory of childhood sexual abuse or other trauma, and where it was later "corroborated" that the traumatic event actually occurred (1-4). Unfortunately, however, these studies suffer from many of the same problems as our study of the mothers above. Here are some examples of these problems.

First, suppose that Ms. A recovers a "memory" that she was sexually abused by Mr. B. Evidence later emerges that Mr. B indisputably abused several other children. Does it follow that Ms. A's "memory" has been now corroborated? No. Ms. A may well have known since her childhood that Mr. B was a bad character, and thus he would be the obvious "candidate" to become the perpetrator in her recovered memory, even if her memory was incorrect and he had never abused her at all. Thus, the discovery that Mr. B has abused other people does not corroborate that he abused Ms. A; rather, Mr. B's conduct may simply confirm something that Ms. A knew, or at least sensed, about him before she ever formed her "memory."

Now, suppose that Mr. C reports to the police that he has just recovered a memory that as an altar boy 20 years ago, he was sexually abused by Reverend D. An investigation ensues, and Reverend D actually confesses to the crime. Unlike the previous example, here we have clear corroboration. But now we have a different problem: we cannot establish whether Mr. C actually repressed his memory, or merely claimed to have repressed it when in fact he remembered it all along. For example, Mr. C might need to allege repression in order to "toll" the statute of limitations and be able to sue Mr. D in court. Or more simply, Mr. C may have been embarrassed to disclose this homosexual encounter to anybody for the last 20 years. He may even have tried hard not to think about it himself. But he never truly forgot it. Now, rather than admit that he never told anyone, it is easier to simply claim that he "repressed" it.

Next, suppose that Ms. E, a patient on a ward specializing in posttraumatic stress disorder, remembers that she was sexually abused as a child by Mr. F. Evidence shows that the abuse really happened. Although she remembers the event currently, Ms. E tells her psychotherapist that she had no memory of the abuse until a year prior to her present hospital admission. Did Ms. E repress the memory? Again we cannot assume so; this case is just another example of the "do-you-remember-whether-you-forgot" type, which we discussed in the previous chapter.

Of course, these scenarios are speculative. Perhaps Ms. A, Mr. C, and Ms. E really did repress their memories. But the point is that one cannot discriminate, in retrospective situations like these, whether repression did or did not occur. For this reason, as in many other areas of scientific study, retrospective studies are untrustworthy (5).

It might seem that we are imposing impossibly high standards on these retrospective designs. Do we have an "agenda" to discredit these studies simply because we do not like what they found? No; we are simply recognizing that years of experience, throughout many fields of science, have shown that any lesser standards would be naive. Faulty conclusions from retrospective reports arise frequently in science, and often create sad consequences. Periodically, for example, a report will appear stating that patients with cancer or AIDS have benefitted from some new drug or herb. Many people do not stop to consider that patients with cancer and AIDS, in the normal course of their diseases, frequently show periods of temporary improvement by chance alone. Instead, it is more appealing to believe that the drug or herb was responsible. Victims of the disease flock to obtain the treatment, even if they must fly to Mexico or obtain it on the black market. Eventually, someone performs a legitimate prospective study of the treatment, assigning one group of subjects to the treatment and the other group to an inert placebo—and the "cure" proves valueless.

The same logic applies in testing the theory that it is possible to repress the memory of a traumatic event. Further retrospective reports, based on cases like those described above, do almost nothing to advance our knowledge on this topic—any more than would additional retrospective accounts claiming that schizophrenia was cured with megavitamins, cancer with laetrile, or AIDS with Chinese herbs. It is time to test the repression hypothesis in properly designed prospective studies.

REFERENCES

1.   Herman JL, Harvey M. Adult memories of childhood trauma. Paper presented at Trauma and Memory: An International Research Conference, Durham, New Hampshire, July 26-28, 1996.

2.   Kluft RP. True lies, false truth, and naturalistic raw data: Applying clinical research findings to the false memory debate. Paper presented at Trauma and Memory: An International Research Conference, Durham, New Hampshire, July 26-28, 1996.

3.   Whitfield CL, Stock WE. Traumatic memories in 50 adult survivors of child sexual abuse. Paper presented at Trauma and Memory: An International Research Conference, Durham, New Hampshire, July 26-28, 1996.

4.   Grassian S, Holtzen D. Memory of sexual abuse by a parish priest. Paper presented at Trauma and Memory: An International Research Conference, Durham, New Hampshire, July 26-28, 1996.

5.   A large literature has addressed the pitfalls of retrospective designs. Some of these will be discussed in the second section of this book, where we consider retrospective studies of childhood sexual abuse and adult psychopathology. For an excellent general discussion of common logical flaws in retrospective analyses, written for the lay reader, see: Gilovich T. How We Know What Isn't So: The Fallibility of Human Reason in Everyday Life. New York: The Free Press, 1991.

8

THE PLAYGROUND STUDY

W E RETURN AGAIN to the age-old question, discussed in the previous chapter, of whether failure to wear a jacket can bring on the common cold. Having witnessed the fallibility of retrospective designs, as illustrated by our questionnaire study of the mothers, we resolve to conduct a more rigorous investigation, this time with a prospective approach. On the next bright, cold winter day, we visit local playgrounds, and without much difficulty, recruit a large sample of children who have forgotten their jackets. We then re-examine the children a week later, and find that they have a rate of colds no higher than any other children. Our prospective study has failed to provide support for the jacket hypothesis. And our new conclusions are clearly far more reliable than those of the old retrospective study in which we merely questioned the mothers.

By analogy, then, the proper way to test the repression hypothesis would be to design a study that is not dependent on anybody's unconfirmed recollections of events. Such a design would not be difficult, although of course one would have to take suitable ethical precautions to protect the safety and confidentiality of the study subjects. First, one would obtain the names of a large group of people who had undergone a known, documented trauma. For example, one could go to the records of a hospital emergency room to find 50 patients who were seen for trauma—severe injuries, physical abuse, or sexual abuse—and where there were specific medical findings in the records to show that the trauma actually occurred. Alternatively, one could identify 50 patients who underwent a traumatic medical procedure, such as a painful rectal or gynecologic examination. One could get 50 assault or rape victims from police records, 50 victims of a tornado, or any other group where the facts of their personal traumatic experience were known and documented. Then, one would locate all of these trauma victims months or years later, interview them, and ask them if they remembered the traumatic event. If a certain percentage of the subjects reported that they had completely forgotten the event, then we would have strong evidence that some people can repress the memory of trauma. On the other hand, if none of the subjects in any of the studies reported forgetting the trauma, then we would suspect that repression does not really happen—except, of course, in the movies.

We would have to be careful about several confounding effects in such a study. The first is the normal amnesia of early childhood. If someone has no memory of having been brought to the emergency ward at age 1 or 2, such a case clearly provides no evidence of repression. Everybody has amnesia for practically all events before the age of 3, and even for most events before age 6 (1). Second, we would have to exclude neurological or medical causes of amnesia. If an individual was knocked unconscious in an accident, or if she received anesthesia for a medical procedure, we would expect her to have amnesia for simple biological reasons alone (2). Similarly, combat veterans would represent a poor choice for our study, because head injuries, severe sleep deprivation, and other neurological insults are so common in wartime (3). Third, we would not want to study people with only mild trauma, because then we could not rule out the possibility that the subject was just experiencing ordinary forgetfulness for an event that was not particularly memorable. In other words, to test whether one can truly repress a memory, we would have to study a group of subjects who experienced a trauma that no ordinary person would be expected to forget. Fourth, when we interviewed our subjects to ask them about their memories, we would have to take care to make sure that they were disclosing all that they remembered. We will discuss this issue in detail in Chapters 9 and 10, but an example will suffice here. Suppose that a girl undergoes a painful and embarrassing gynecologic procedure at age 10. When she reaches age 15, a researcher sees her for an interview and asks her if she has undergone any unusual medical procedures. Even if the interviewer is careful and sympathetic, the girl may still answer, "no," even though she actually remembers the event. To minimize such non-disclosure, the interviewer may need to ask the subject about the specific event in a more direct manner: "I know from your medical records that when you were 10, you were seen at the hospital for a special medical examination. Do you remember that?"

In summary, then, a satisfactory scientific test of repression would have to follow only a couple of simple rules: 1) locate a group of people who were victims of a documented trauma, and 2) interview them some years later to see if any of them report amnesia for the trauma. We would exclude cases where the failure to report might be due to a) early childhood amnesia, b) neurological or medical causes, c) ordinary forgetfulness, or d) deliberate non-disclosure. If after these exclusions, we were still left with a fair number of patients who described amnesia for the event, we would have evidence that repression really does occur.

Those are the ground rules. What is the verdict? To our knowl-

edge every study in the world literature that has come even re-
motely close to the above standards has *failed to show any evidence that people can repress memories*.

Here are some examples. In the 1960's, Leopold and Dillon
(4) studied 34 men who had survived a terrible explosion when
two ships collided. In interviews conducted about 4 years after
the explosion, many of the men reported serious posttraumatic
psychopathology, but none displayed amnesia. The authors wrote,
"repression does not appear possible." In another study, Terr (5,
6) interviewed 25 children who had been kidnapped and buried
alive in a school bus 4 years earlier. She found that "each child
could give a fully detailed account of the experience." (Terr was
not surprised at this finding because the kidnapping was what she
calls a "type I" trauma, as we have explained in Chapter 4). Malt
(7) interviewed 107 individuals who had been seen at an emergency ward for traumatic injuries 16 to 51 months previously.
The only amnesia found in these individuals was that due to neurological injuries; no one was described as having repressed the
memory. Wagenaar and Groeneweg (8) recruited 78 subjects who
were involved in a Nazi war crimes trial in the 1980s, and asked
them about their memories of having been in a concentration camp
40 years earlier. Although many of the subjects were quite elderly
by the 1980s, most remembered the camp "in great detail." The
subjects had forgotten various specific experiences, but they had
forgotten non-traumatic events just as often as traumatic ones;
there was no evidence that they had selectively repressed traumatic memories. Interestingly, there were 6 men who had testi-
fied to various specific traumatic experiences when they were
originally liberated from the camp in the 1940s, but who did not
describe these memories when they were re-interviewed in the
1980s. However, when they were reminded of their earlier testimony, all but one of them promptly recalled the particular events.

This is a remarkable record considering that these former inmates were 65 to 82 years old by the 1980s—and hence vulnerable to the biologically based forgetfulness of old age. Peterson and Bell (9) interviewed 90 children who had been seen at a hospital in Newfoundland for traumatic injuries 6 months earlier. It appears that every child, including even those only 2 years old at the time, remembered the event. Among the children who were 9 to 13 years old at the time of their injuries, so few made errors of recall that the investigators did not even include them in a statistical analysis of the causes of errors of memory.

The above studies span a range of traumas, from single events like the marine explosion to longstanding events like the concentration camp experience. Some of the subjects in some of the studies had spoken at length about their experiences to other people, or undergone prior interviews, and hence might be expected to have particularly clear memories. On the other hand, some of the subjects were being studied for the first time, and had had no opportunity to "rehearse" their memories previously. But the one feature shared by the subjects in every study was that, when asked, they remembered their trauma.

Some critics might still object to our evidence here. They would argue that explosions, kidnappings, concentration camps, and hospital visits are very different from "secret" traumas such as childhood sexual abuse. Even allowing that repression does not occur for ordinary traumas, perhaps it might still occur in certain special situations, like that of a child who is forced to undergo repeated sexual assaults from someone whom she is supposed to love. Therefore, rather than be too quick to dismiss the possibility of repression, we owe it to ourselves to examine prospective studies that look specifically at the memories of the victims of childhood sexual abuse. We will do this in the next two chapters.

REFERENCES

1. For typical studies of early childhood amnesia see: Kihlstrom JF, Harackiewicz JM. The earliest recollection: A new survey. J Pers 50:134-148, 1982; Howe ML, Courage ML. On resolving the enigma of infantile amnesia. Psychol Bull 113:305-326, 1993; Fivush R, Hudson JA, eds. Knowing and Remembering in Young Children. New York: Cambridge Univ Press, 1990; and Usher JA, Neisser V. Childhood amnesia and the beginnings of memory for four early life events. J Exp Psychology 122:155-165, 1993.

2. Note that even a head injury that does not cause unconsciousness may sometimes cause amnesia for periods as long as a year. For example, see: Stracciari A, Ghidoni E, Guarino M, Poletti M, Pazzaglia P. Post-traumatic retrograde amnesia with selective impairment of autobiographical memory. Cortex 30:459-468, 1994. For more general information on biological causes of amnesia see: Forrester G, Encel J, Geffen G. Measuring post-traumatic amnesia (PATA): An historical review. Brain Inj 8:175-184, 1994. See also: Squire LR. Memory and Brain. New York: Oxford, 1987.

3. Studies of combat victims suffer not only from the pervasive problem of biological amnesia, but also from possible false memories induced by barbiturate-facilitated interviewing (for example, see: Grinker RR, Spiegel JP. Men Under Stress. Philadelphia: Blakiston, 1945), from possible false claims of amnesia by soldiers who actually remember (Kalman G. On combat-neurosis: Psychiatric experience during the recent Middle-East War. J Soc Psychiatry 23:195-203, 1977), and from cases of amnesia when there was no apparent trauma (Fisher C. Amnesic states in war neuroses: The psychogenesis of fugues. Psychoanalytic Quarterly 14:437-468, 1945). Further, many war studies are merely collections of case reports, and thus, do not represent acceptable tests of the repression hypothesis, as we have explained previously in Chapter 5.

4. Leopold RL, Dillon H. Psycho-anatomy of a disaster: A long-term study of post-traumatic neuroses in survivors of a marine explosion. Am J Psychiatry 119:913-921, 1963.

5. Terr LC. Children of Chowchilla: A study of psychic trauma. Psychoanal Study Child 34:552-623, 1979.

6. Terr LC. Chowchilla revisited: The effects of psychic trauma four years after a school-bus kidnapping. Am J Psychiatry 140:1543-1550, 1983.

7.   Malt U. The long-term psychiatric consequences of accidental injury: A longitudinal study of 107 adults. Br J Psychiatry 153:810-818, 1988.

8.   Wagenaar WA, Groeneweg J. The memory of concentration camp survivors. Appl Cognitive Psychology 4:77-87, 1990.

9.   Peterson C, Bell M. Children's memory for trauma injury. Child Develop 67:3045-3070, 1996.

9

'Cuz I Wanted to Forget

In THE PREVIOUS CHAPTER, we have seen that prospective studies of trauma victims consistently fail to show evidence of repression. But there remain to our knowledge four other published prospective studies that have looked specifically at memories of childhood sexual abuse. If repression can be found anywhere, perhaps these studies are the place to look.

The first such study was published in 1990 by Donna Della Femina and her colleagues (1). These investigators interviewed 69 young adults in Connecticut as part of a follow-up study of formerly incarcerated youths. The investigators possessed detailed information, obtained in evaluations many years earlier, about physical and sexual abuse that these subjects had endured as children. Upon interviewing these subjects as young adults, the investigators found that 26, or 38% of them, reported childhood histories that were inconsistent with the information that had been gathered on these earlier evaluations. Specifically, 18 of these 26 subjects were known to have been severely abused in childhood, yet they denied or minimized any history of abuse when they were interviewed as young adults. The other 8 subjects had not reported abuse during their initial evaluations, yet described experiences of child-hood abuse when interviewed by Femina and her colleagues. Is it possible, then, that the 18 non-reporting subjects had repressed the memory of the abuse that they were known to have experienced? And had the other 8 subjects, who suddenly revealed new informa-tion about childhood abuse, recovered old memories that had been repressed at the time of their initial evaluations?

Fortunately, Femina and her colleagues did not jump to these conclusions. Instead, they attempted to re-contact the 26 subjects who had given interview information discrepant with their earlier evaluations. They managed to locate 11 of the 26 for a second inter-view, which they called the "clarification" interview. In the clarifica-tion interview, they took care to establish rapport, and then confronted the subjects with the known discrepancies in their responses.

In the clarification interview, it appears, all 11 of the subjects admitted that they had always remembered their abuse, but had simply chosen not to disclose the information, either during their interview with Femina and her co-workers (for the 8 subjects who denied their previously recorded history of abuse), or on their ini-tial evaluation (for the 3 subjects who revealed new information about abuse not recorded on their initial evaluation). When asked to explain the reasons that they had chosen to withhold the infor-mation, the subjects gave a variety of responses. For example, one girl, who was known to have been sexually abused by her father, and whose mother had attempted to drown her as a child, mini-mized any abuse at all in the initial interview. When asked later in the clarification interview why she did not previously disclose the information, she burst into tears and said, "I didn't say it 'cuz I wanted to forget. I wanted it to be private. I only cry when I think about it." Similarly a boy, who had been repeatedly beaten by his psychotic father, denied abuse in his initial interview but then ad-mitted to it in the clarification interview. When asked why, he said,

"My father is doing well now. If I told now, I think he would kill himself." Another subject, who had also initially failed to disclose a known history of physical abuse, explained in the clarification interview that he had simply not liked the original interviewer.

Finally, looking at the 3 subjects who described histories of abuse in interviews that were not recorded in their initial evaluations, the investigators again found that deliberate non-disclosure, rather than repression, was responsible for the discrepancies. Two of the subjects revealed that, at the time of their earlier evaluations, they were too embarrassed to reveal what they had suffered. The third had refused to disclose his abuse at the time because he did not trust anybody.

In summary, then, the investigators documented many reasons why subjects might not reveal a history of childhood sexual or physical abuse when interviewed. These included "embarrassment, a wish to protect parents, a sense of having deserved the abuse, a conscious wish to forget the past, and a lack of rapport with the interviewer." In no instance, however, was any subject found to have displayed repression.

What is the lesson of this? It is that people will sometimes choose not to disclose information, especially sensitive and embarrassing information like a history of childhood sexual abuse, in interviews. If this happens, it would be naive for us to jump to the conclusion that they have repressed their memories. Instead, as illustrated by Femina and her colleagues, it is critical to ask any nondisclosing subjects *directly* about their known trauma history, to see whether they will then acknowledge that they remember it.

The same considerations apply to a second recent study conducted in London, where investigators interviewed 20 women who had been removed from their homes as children by social service agencies (2). These women were known to have been sexually abused, both from their own reports as children and by the report of an adult who had been familiar with the household at the time. The follow-up interviews were conducted when the subjects were 18-24 years old. In these interviews, 3 (15%) of the 20 women failed to answer "yes" to the question, "Were you sexually abused as a child?" However, in this case, by the author's admission, none of the subjects was directly asked about her known sexual abuse history, and no "clarification interviews" were conducted later. Therefore, when it is considered that the rate of negative responses in this study was well below the 38% rate in the Femina study described above, it again seems that these findings can be easily explained on the basis of non-disclosure alone, with no need to postulate repression.

We should digress a moment here to explain this last phrase. When we say, "no need to postulate repression," we are referring to the fundamental scientific principle of *parsimony*. This principle states that if a phenomenon can already be well explained by a known and proven phenomenon (such as non-disclosure, in this case), there is no need to invoke a new and unproven phenomenon (such as repression) to explain the findings. By analogy, if our car dies on the highway, we should not invoke some novel theory— such as fouling of the car's spark plugs by ambient electromagnetic radiation—until we have ruled out more mundane and proven possibilities, such as running out of gas.

Returning to the question of repression, there is one other recent small study that followed up on 22 children who had reportedly been abused in one of three day-care centers (3). Again, three of the children were said to display complete amnesia for their abuse when interviewed 5 to 10 years later. However, in this case there is a different problem: the children were reported to be a median of 2 1/2 years old at the time of the original alleged abuse. Among the examples provided in the study, one child was in day care between the ages of 6 weeks and 12 months of age; another was 21 months old. As we have mentioned in the previous chapter, there is a large literature showing that children remember almost nothing from before the age of 3, much less at 12 or 21 months. Thus the findings in this study appear readily explainable on the basis of childhood amnesia alone, again without any need to postulate repression. In addition, there remains the possibility of deliberate non-disclosure in this study as well, but the issue is not mentioned in the paper.

In summary, these three follow-up studies of victims of childhood sexual and physical abuse all fail to produce any evidence of repression. As Femina and her colleagues so clearly demonstrated in their "clarification interviews," cases of seeming repression on initial interview regularly turn out to represent deliberate non-disclosure.

This leaves us with only one remaining prospective study of victims of childhood sexual abuse—our last chance, in effect, to find an acceptable demonstration of repression in the scientific literature. But this study, performed by Linda Meyer Williams, is perhaps the most widely quoted study of them all. If there is any study that provides legitimate evidence of repression, many experts would say, the Williams study would be the one. Therefore, the Williams study deserves a particularly careful analysis in a chapter all to itself.

REFERENCES

1. Femina DD, Yeager CA, Lewis DO. Child abuse: Adolescent records vs. adult recall. Child Abuse Negl 145:227-231, 1990.

2. Bagley C. Child Sexual Abuse and Mental Health in Adolescents and Adults: British and Canadian Perspectives. Aldershot, UK: Avebury, 1995.

3. Burgess AW, Hartman CR, Baker T. Memory presentations of childhood sexual abuse. J Psychosocial Nursing 33:9-16, 1995.

10

GARBAGE IN, GARBAGE OUT

LITTLE NOTICED IN THE annals of social science research, but good reading for any beginning student of psychology, is the Tucson Garbage Project (1). In this study, a group of archeologists decided to study the garbage discarded by randomly selected households in Tucson, Arizona, during 1973 and 1974. Over 70 student volunteers, dressed in lab coats, surgical masks, and gloves, sorted through the garbage of 624 Tucson households and divided the refuse into more than 200 categories. Meanwhile, a group of trained personnel went out and interviewed individuals in a random sample of 1% of the households in the city. The interviewers asked, among other questions, how many cans or bottles of beer were consumed in the household in an average week. Then, the data from each of Tucson's census tracts were analyzed. The average reported weekly beer consumption of all households in a given census tract (standardized as the number of 12-ounce bottles or cans) was compared with the actual number of bottles and cans found in the pooled garbage for that census tract.

The reader can probably guess what happened. The number of beer cans and bottles in the garbage vastly exceeded the number that people had admitted to in their interviews. Looking, for example, at Tucson's census tract number 10, more than 86% of the households reported to interviewers that they did not consume any beer at all in an average week, and not a single household (out of 60 interviewed) claimed a weekly consumption of more than eight cans. But the garbage from tract 10 told another story. Only 23% of households had no beer cans in their garbage, whereas 54% of households had more than eight cans. In fact, the average number of cans in the garbage from that 54% of households was 15 per week—in other words, 2 1/2 six-packs. And even these findings may underestimate the true discrepancy between interview data and actual beer consumption, because in 1973 most beer cans in Tucson were recyclable.

What does this have to do with studies of repression? Those who have read the previous two chapters will quickly recognize the point: people regularly fail to disclose sensitive information to interviewers. Like the subjects in the Femina study, who chose not to reveal their histories of childhood physical and sexual abuse, the people of Tucson were unwilling to tell an interviewer their true consumption of beer. They had not repressed the memory of all those six-packs; they just did not want to tell a stranger about it.

As with other concepts in epidemiology discussed elsewhere in this book, this phenomenon of underreporting has a name: *response bias*. Response bias has been studied extensively for at least 50 years, and we now know a great deal about it. But before continuing with this discussion, we must take some time out to introduce the one remaining prospective study claiming to show that people repress memories of childhood sexual abuse—the study of Linda Meyer Williams (2).

Some readers will already have heard of the Williams study. It is regularly cited as the single most powerful piece of evidence that it is actually possible to repress memories. Frequently, in the popular media, in scientific articles, and even in courtrooms, the study is cited as though its findings were established, without even a passing consideration of the possibility that it has methodological flaws (3). But these flaws are so critical that they deserve a careful review, and hence we describe the methods of the study in some detail.

Williams studied 129 women who had been evaluated at a city hospital in Philadelphia in the early 1970s for possible sexual abuse. At the time of that evaluation, which might be called the "index episode," these subjects were young girls between 10 months and 12 years of age. Williams possessed the hospital records from this "index episode." Then, approximately 17 years after the time of the index episode, Williams arranged for two interviewers to locate these women and question them about their histories. The women were not informed that the investigators were specifically looking at their histories of childhood sexual abuse; they were simply told that they were being asked to participate in an important follow-up study of people who had been seen years earlier at the city hospital. During the course of the interview, each woman was asked about various types of traumatic experiences that she might have experienced during childhood, including sexual abuse. The interviewers also asked the women to describe any episodes that they themselves had not considered to be sexual abuse, but that other people had considered as such. However—and this is the important part—the two investigators interviewing the women were "blinded" to all information about the women's sexual abuse history; in other words, they had no knowledge of the specifics of the "index episode" when they interviewed their subjects, and therefore they asked the subjects only in general terms about sexual abuse. The subjects *were never specifically asked about the index episode itself.*

Forty-nine, or 38% of the 129 women did not describe the index episode of alleged sexual abuse in the course of the interview. Williams suggests in her paper that these women "did not recall" the episode. She supports this interpretation by noting that many of the women reported other traumatic events, or sensitive details of their histories—such as substance abuse, sexually transmitted diseases, and even other instances of physical or sexual abuse—while still not reporting the index episode. Therefore, Williams argues, it seems likely that the women would have reported the index episode if they had remembered it.

But can we conclude that any of these 49 women had actually repressed the memory of the index episode? Several serious methodological concerns immediately become apparent. First, only 37, or 28% of the 129 women displayed genital trauma when they were examined by the doctors at the time of the index evaluation. By contrast, as the reader may recall from Chapter 6, studies by gynecologists have shown that as many as 96% of girls subjected to genito-genital contact will display genital tract findings even on a simple visual medical examination (4). Clearly, something is wrong here. It appears that a majority of Williams' subjects, if they were sexually abused, were not victims of genito-genital penetration.

Williams admits to this. In another paper, in fact, she notes that approximately one third of the cases involved only "touching and fondling"(5). And in an earlier description of this same sample of subjects, written back in 1979, Williams and her colleagues imply that for many of the girls, the alleged instance of sexual abuse was not particularly traumatic and therefore not particularly memorable:

Whereas the event [*the index episode*] is disturbing to the victim, it is perhaps no more disturbing than so many other aspects of a child's life. In the first year following the rape [*in the broad, statutory definition of the term, which includes touching or fondling*], the victim's family may deliberately maintain an "everything-is-normal" posture. These efforts, combined with the child's natural tendencies to forget and to replace bad feelings with good feelings, usually result in the appearance of few adjustment problems . . . (6; bracketed inserts ours).

In other words, looking both at the lack of medical evidence and at Williams' own words, it seems that many of these girls may have experienced episodes that were not particularly severe. An episode of only touching and fondling, without any medical evidence of penetration, might not be perceived as particularly traumatic or particularly memorable to a young child, even though an adult might recognize the episode as clear sexual abuse. When we consider that Williams herself found these episodes "no more disturbing than many other aspects of a child's life," and subject to "the child's natural tendencies to forget," it becomes clear that many of the women, interviewed 17 years later, might simply have forgotten the event. They had not repressed the memory of the index episode; it had simply seemed too minor to be worth remembering.

Of course, we can debate back and forth the question of how many of the women might fall into this category. But at the least, it seems clear that the most scientifically valid approach would be to restrict our analysis in the Williams study to the 37 women who did show evidence of genital trauma at the time of the index evaluation. These represent the cases where there can be no dispute that serious sexual abuse really occurred, and where the victim would not be expected simply to forget. Among these 37 cases, we are left with 18 who failed to report the episode in the follow-up interview.

But this number may need to be reduced even further when we allow for the effects of early childhood amnesia. Recall that the subjects were as little as 10 months old at the time of the index episode. As we have mentioned in Chapter 8, failure to recall an event from one's infancy clearly does not represent evidence of repression. Looking at Williams' data, we find that about one quarter of the total sample of 49 non-reporting women were aged 4 years or younger at the time of the index episode. Applying this ratio to the subgroup of 18 cases described above, we would estimate that there were only about 14 women who 1) had medically documented genital trauma; 2) were old enough to remember the experience; and 3) did not report the experience in the follow-up interview 17 years later.

Thus, we are down to about 14 subjects in the only study that we have left to analyze. The case for repression of memories of childhood sexual abuse, in short, now hangs on these 14 people. But we have not yet considered the problem raised at the beginning of this chapter—response bias.

When we factor in response bias, what is left of the case for "repressed memory" collapses completely. Remember that none of the subjects in the study was ever asked directly whether she remembered the known index episode. None of the non-reporting subjects was ever given a "clarification interview" at a later date in the manner of the Femina et al. study described in the previous chapter. Remember also that 38% of the subjects in the Femina study chose not to disclose their history of abuse during an initial interview—but when given clarification interviews, 100% revealed that they actually remembered. When we consider the roughly 14 still unexplained cases out of the 129 subjects in the Williams study, we see that this number falls well within the range to be expected from non-disclosure alone—indeed, it is surprisingly small—without any need to claim the existence of repression.

Response bias due to non-disclosure is a well recognized problem in social science research, documented in hundreds of studies spanning many decades throughout the last 50 years. In 1956, for example, the United States Congress authorized a continuing program of health surveys by the Public Health Service to provide reliable statistical information about the health status of the United

States population. This mandate produced a long series of studies over the next 20 years, in which scientists examined the accuracy of survey methodology. They found that people, even when carefully interviewed by trained personnel, consistently underreported life events that were known to have occurred. In one study, for example, 28% of subjects failed to report a one-day hospitalization that they were known to have undergone within the past year (7). In another, approximately 30% of subjects did not disclose a car accident (without head injury or loss of consciousness) that was documented to have occurred 9 to 12 months previously (8). In yet another study, 35% of subjects did not report a doctor's visit that they were known to have made just within the last 2 weeks (9). Clearly, these subjects had not repressed the memory of having just gone to the doctor; the interviewers were simply witnessing response bias.

The scientists in these studies performed numerous analyses to determine what caused underreporting of life events (10). They found, for example, that people were more likely to withhold information about undesirable, threatening, or sensitive material as opposed to neutral material. They also discovered that non-disclosure of information was generally more common among non-White subjects then among White subjects, and more common among subjects of lower socioeconomic class than among subjects of higher socioeconomic class. It is worth noting, in this connection, that Williams' subjects (in the study introduced on page 62) were mostly African-American women of lower socioeconomic class. And it need hardly be added that childhood sexual abuse would certainly rank among the most sensitive categories of information.

Another typical study of response bias is the National Crime Survey (11). Several studies in this survey used a "reverse record" system to validate reports of victimization. This technique involved sampling victims of crime from a record system, such as police files, and then locating the victims and interviewing them using a survey questionnaire. Information from interviews was then compared to actual records to establish the accuracy of the survey instrument. The studies consistently found that victims failed to disclose crimes which they had recently experienced. In one study in Baltimore, for example, victims underreported burglaries by 14%, robberies by 24%, larceny by 25%, and assault by 64%. In another study in San Jose, assault was underreported by 52% and rape by 33%. In several of the studies, the interviewers probed the victims for detailed histories, while still not directly confronting the subjects regarding the known crime. But even with probing, high rates of underreporting persisted. Again, there is nothing to suggest that these people repressed the memory of the crimes; a certain percentage of them simply withheld the information on interview.

The list of studies of non-disclosure goes on and on (12). In every study, people have been found to underreport sensitive or embarrassing information of all types, such as alcohol consumption (13), drug use (14), having declared bankruptcy (15), drunk driving charges (15), arrest records (16), HIV infection (17), other medical conditions (18), psychiatric history (19), and, of course, childhood sexual abuse (20-22). Indeed, in one of these latter studies (21), no less than 72% of 116 self-acknowledged victims of childhood sexual abuse said that they had denied their history of abuse when initially interviewed—a figure even more striking than the 38% non-disclosure rate in the Femina study. The recurring theme from all of this literature is obvious: when interviewees fail to report sensitive information from their histories, the investigators should immediately suspect response bias. Until they have addressed this problem (for example, by means of clarification interviews), it would be very hazardous for them to assume that their subjects have forgotten (much less repressed) the information.

We return now to the Williams study discussed at the beginning of this chapter. Remarkably, Williams does not mention any of the literature on non-disclosure that we have briefly reviewed above. Even the Femina study is not cited. Of course, Williams admits that none of her subjects was directly asked about the known index episode. She also admits to the existence of response bias. But she does not seem to acknowledge that the women in her own study might have chosen to withhold information about their index episode of childhood sexual abuse. If 35% of interviewees in a government study fail to disclose a simple doctor's visit occurring within the last two weeks, and if 64% of recent assault victims fail to describe the crime even when interviewed in detail, how many victims of childhood sexual abuse, interviewed by an unfamiliar person, of higher socioeconomic class, 17 years later, might choose to withhold information that they actually remembered?

And if this is not enough, it is worth noting that Williams herself is an author of a large review article that seems to contradict the conclusions of her own study (23). In collaboration with two other authors, she reviewed the aftereffects of childhood sexual abuse in 45 studies examining 3369 victims. As far as can be seen from the review, none of the victims in any of these studies was described as showing repression.

In a word, then, despite its wide publicity and frequent uncritical acceptance, we believe that the Williams study suffers from methodological problems that collectively render its results completely inadequate as a demonstration of repression. Indeed, when we add together the effects of lack of documentation, ordinary forgetfulness, childhood amnesia, and deliberate non-disclosure, it seems remarkable that *only* 38% of the women failed to report the index episode. Taking it the other way, the observation that a full 62% of the women described an event that had occurred 17 years earlier—in the face of all of these opposing factors, and even when they were not asked specifically about it—would seem to weigh *against* the possibility that repression occurs.

In conclusion, we do not mean to be unduly harsh on Williams. Her study methodology is far superior to most of the studies of repression discussed earlier. But the study is still subject to certain methodological limitations, especially response bias. In short, when assessing any prospective study of this type, the reader would be wise to remember the Tucson Garbage Project.

REFERENCES

1. Rathje WL, Hughes WW. The Garbage Project as a nonreactive approach: Garbage in . . . garbage out? In Sinaiko HW, Broedlins LA, eds. Perspectives on Attitude Assessment: Surveys and Their Alternatives. Washington, DC: Smithsonian Institution, 1975.

2. Williams LM. Recall of childhood trauma: A prospective study of women's memories of child sexual abuse. J Consult Clin Psychology 62:1167-1176, 1994.

3. For a detailed discussion of the misuse of the Williams study in courtrooms, see: Hagen MA. Whores of the Court: The Fraud of Psychiatric Testimony and the Rape of American Justice. New York: Regan Books, 1997.

4. Muram D. Child sexual abuse—Genital tract findings in prepubertal girls. I: The unaided medical examination. Am J Obstet Gynecol 160:328-333, 1989.

5. Williams LM. Adult memories of child sexual abuse: Preliminary findings from a longitudinal study. American Society for Prevention of Child Abuse Advisor 5:19-20, 1992.

6. McCahill TW, Meyer LC, Fischman AM. The Aftermath of Rape. Lexington, MA: Lexington Books, 1979.

7. National Center for Health Statistics. Reporting of Hospitalization in the Health Interview Survey. Washington, DC: U.S. Dept. of Health, Education, and Welfare, PHS Pub. No. 584-D4, May 1961.

8. National Center for Health Statistics. Optimum Recall Period for Reporting Persons Injured in Motor Vehicle Accidents. Washington, DC: U.S.

Dept. of Health, Education, and Welfare, DHEW Pub. No. (HSM) 72-1050, April 1972.

9. National Center for Health Statistics. Health Interview Responses Compared with Medical Records. Washington, DC: U.S. Dept. of Health, Education, and Welfare, PHS Pub. No. 1000-Series 2-No. 7, July 1965.

10. National Center for Health Statistics. A Summary of Studies of Interviewing Methodology. Washington, DC: U.S. Dept. of Health, Education, and Welfare, DHEW Pub. No. (HRA) 77-1343, March 1977.

11. Lehnen RG, Skogan WG, eds. The National Crime Survey: Working Papers, Vol. I. Current and Historical Perspectives.Washington, DC: U.S. Department of Justice, Bureau of Justice Statistics, NCJ-75374, December 1981.

12. Numerous reviews and entire books have been written about non-disclosure and other pitfalls of interviewing techniques. See for example: Taner JM, ed. Questions about Questions. New York: Russell Sage Foundation, 1992; Mangione TW, Hingson R, Barrett J. Collecting sensitive data. Soc Methods Res 10:337-346, 1982; Belson WA. Validity in Survey Research. Aldershot, UK: Gower, 1986; Fowler FJ. Improving Survey Questions: Design and Evaluation. Thousand Oaks, CA: Sage Publications, 1995; Fowler FJ. Survey Research Methods. 2d ed. Newbury Park: Sage Publications, 1993. See pp. 69-93; and Zdep SM, Rhodes IN, Schwarz RM, Kilkenny MJ. The validity of the randomized response technique. In Singer E, Presser S, eds. Survey Research Methods: A Reader. Chicago: Univ of Chicago Press, 1989.

13. See among many studies in this area: Polich JM, Armor D, Braiker HB. The Course of Alcoholism: Four Years after Treatment. Santa Monica: The Rand Corporation, 1979; Cooke DJ, Allan CA. Self-reported alcohol consumption and dissimulation in a Scottish urban sample. J Stud Alcohol 4: 617-629, 1983; and many other such studies reviewed by: Midanic LT. Validity of self-reported alcohol use: A literature review and assessment. Br J Addiction 83:1019-1029, 1988.

14. Among the numerous studies on this topic are: Swerdlow NR, Geyer MA, Perry W, Cadenhead K, Braff DL. Drug screening in "normal" controls. Biol Psychiatry 38:123-124, 1995; and Blynn SM, Gruder CL, Jegerski JA. Effects of biochemical validation of self-reported cigarette smoking on treatment success and on misreporting abstinence. Health Psychology 5:125-136, 1986.

15. Locander W, Sudman S, Bradburn N. An investigation of interview method, threat and response distortion. J Am Stat Assoc 71:269-275, 1971.

16. Tracy PE, Fox JA. The validity of randomized response for sensitive measurements. Am Sociological Rev 46:187-200, 1981.

17. A large literature has arisen in this area. Among the many studies, see: Marks G, Bundek NI, Richardson JL, Ruiz MS, Maldonado N, Mason HR. Self-disclosure of HIV infection: Preliminary results from a sample of Hispanic men. Health Psychology 11:300-306, 1992; and McCarthy GM, Haji FS, Mackie ID. HIV-infected patients and dental care: Nondisclosure of HIV status and rejection for treatment. Oral Surg Oral Med Oral Pathol Oral Radiol Endod 80:655-659, 1995.

18. See, for example: National Center for Health Statistics. Interview Data on Chronic Conditions Compared with Information Derived from Medical Records. Washington, DC: U.S. Dept. of Health, Education, and Welfare, PHS Pub. No. 1000-Series 2-No. 23, May 1967; and Salinsky MC, Wegener K, Sinnema F. Epilepsy, driving laws, and patient disclosure to physicians. Epilepsia 33:469-472, 1992.

19. Examples include: Sacks MH, Gunn JH, Frosch WA. Withholding of information by psychiatric inpatients. Hosp Comm Psychiatry 32:424-425, 1981; and Bennett M, Rutledge J. Self-disclosure in a clinical context by Asian and British psychiatric outpatients. Br J Clin Psychology 28:155-163, 1989.

20. Farrell LR. Factors that affect a victim's self-disclosure in father-daughter incest. Child Welfare League of America 67:462-468, 1988.

21. Sorensen T, Snow B. How children tell: The process of disclosure in child sexual abuse. Child Welfare League of America 70:3-15, 1991.

22. Faulkner N. Sexual Abuse Recognition and Non-disclosure Inventory of Young Adolescents [dissertation]. Ann Arbor, MI: Univ of Michigan, 1996.

23. Kendall-Tackett KA, Williams LM, Finkelhor D. Impact of sexual abuse on children: A review and synthesis of recent empirical studies. Psychol Bull 113:164-180, 1993.

11

THE DAIRY FARMERS AND
THE SEISMOLOGISTS

THE AMERICAN Psychological Association's Working Group on Investigation of Memories of Childhood Abuse has recently released a report of its "final conclusions"(1). Although the Working Group was able to agree on a few basic principles, much of the report is devoted to a discussion of the differences of opinion and perspective between clinicians and researchers. It seems that clinicians on the Working Group favored the hypothesis that memories of traumatic events could be repressed and subsequently recovered, while the researchers were apparently more skeptical of this theory. Reading between the lines of the report, it appears that the clinicians felt they were the people best qualified to discuss the scientific validity of repression and recovered memory, because they saw real trauma victims in practice, whereas the researchers did not. The researchers, conversely, felt that they were the best qualified, since they were the most experienced in designing and evaluating scientific studies.

What is the answer to this dispute? This is an important question, because it affects whether the reader will give credence to the arguments in this book. Clearly, we have taken the "research" position, arguing that careful attention to study methodology is more important than clinical observation in evaluating the validity of the repression hypothesis.

Some examples, we hope, will support our position. Suppose that we were to return to our loyal panel of 100 American mothers, described in Chapter 6, and ask them about the value of chicken soup in the treatment of children with the common cold. We might well receive a strong endorsement of this treatment. However, if we were to put the same question to a panel of microbiologists— people who study infectious diseases—we would find much less consensus. The mothers of America, it is true, have a lot more clinical experience with sick children than the average microbiologist, but we must still conclude that the efficacy of chicken soup in the treatment of the common cold is not scientifically accepted.

Consider another example. If we were to survey California dairy farmers, we might find widespread acceptance of the theory that cows behave strangely prior to earthquakes. However, upon presenting this theory to a group of researchers in seismology, we would probably encounter skepticism. But then, what do seismologists know? Most seismologists probably could not distinguish one end of a dairy cow from another. Obviously it is the "clinicians"—the dairy farmers—who know best.

This last example is not as frivolous as it first seems. The main point, clearly, is that the ability of cows to predict earthquakes is not scientifically accepted. However—and this is important—the dairy farmers could be right. Maybe farm animals can anticipate earthquakes, and perhaps somebody should design a study of this phenomenon. In other words, we should not dismiss the "clinical" impressions of the farmers. But until a properly designed study actually confirms statistically that cows can anticipate earthquakes, we cannot consider the theory to be scientifically accepted (2).

Indeed, we must acknowledge that there are sometimes cases in medicine where "clinicians" have proven right and researchers wrong. For example, coaches and trainers have known since the 1960s that anabolic steroids allow athletes to achieve huge gains in muscle mass, far beyond what can be achieved without these drugs. Yet, for years, researchers in pharmacology and endocrinology argued that steroids did not really work, and that athletes were experiencing just a "placebo effect" (3). We now know, of course, that these earlier researchers were dead wrong (4). It turns out that they were basing their conclusions on studies using doses of steroids far below those used by actual athletes. Also, in many of the studies, issues of diet, prior training, and measurement of strength and muscle mass were not properly addressed (5). However, if we were asked whether the efficacy of anabolic steroids for muscle gains was scientifically accepted in the 1970s, or even in the 1980s, the correct answer would have to be "no." The fact that coaches and trainers "knew" that these drugs worked did not constitute scientific acceptance.

In short, even though the observations of clinicians may prove correct, clinicians alone do not constitute an adequate reference group to assess scientific acceptability. Even if these clinicians have done research, published papers, and given scientific lectures in a particular field, that still does not make them the sole authorities. If we consider such clinicians to be the only appropriate reference group for judging "scientific acceptance," we will make serious mistakes. For example, we would not judge the scientific acceptance of astrology purely on the opinions of professional astrologers, even if they had published authoritative books on astrology and chaired important committees of a prestigious Astrological Association. We would not judge the scientific acceptance of alien abduction by restricting ourselves to clinicians who had actually treated victims of extraterrestrials, even if these clinicians had been plenary speakers at various World Congresses on Alien Visitation. To judge correctly the opinions of the scientific community on these issues, we would also need to include a much broader group of prestigious researchers—people who know how to examine critically a scientific paper, even if they had never done someone's horoscope or published a paper on UFOs.

But there is another analogy that is perhaps even more apt when we discuss the scientific acceptance of repression and recovered memory. That is the theory that sugar and food additives may cause or exacerbate attention-deficit hyperactivity disorder (ADHD) in children. For years, parents, teachers, and school counselors have widely accepted the views of certain clinicians that food additives might have harmful effects on such children (6). Sugar, similarly, has been widely indicted clinically as causing hyperactive behavior (7). Primary care physicians, who have extensive clinical experience with such children, frequently recommend restricting their sugar intake (8). But is the link between diet and hyperactivity scientifically accepted? Numerous careful *prospective* scientific studies have now appeared, in which sugar or food additives were given to hyperactive children under rigorous placebo-controlled, double-blind conditions (9-12). The results have resoundingly demonstrated that sugar and food additives have no consistent effect on ADHD. In other words, if we assumed that clinicians who treated actual hyperactive children were the best authorities on the subject, we would have seriously misrepresented what science actually knows.

In the ongoing debate about repression and recovered memory, therefore, clinicians may have a great deal to contribute, but they have no special authority to tell us whether these concepts are scientifically accepted. As the above examples have suggested, clinicians may be right or they may be wrong about a particular theory. Their experience with treating and studying actual patients is unquestionably an asset. If they have published papers in the field, so much the better. But their clinical work may also act as a deficit, particularly if it leads them to become personally invested in a hypothesis, and reluctant to acknowledge opposing data. Thus, an accurate assessment of the scientific acceptance of a given hypothesis must be based on a careful and uncompromising review of the research literature, by scientists who are familiar with the strengths and weakness of the methodology of the various studies.

We have tried to provide just such an assessment in these 11 essays. As we have attempted to illustrate, the hypothesis that people can repress memories of traumatic events—however appealing it may be as a romantic notion, however often we see it in popular books and movies, and however many clinicians claim to "know" it from experience—does not even come close to meeting the necessary standards for scientific acceptance. Of course, like the dairy cows who seem to anticipate earthquakes, the hypothesis of repression may eventually be proven. But from a scientific standpoint, it would still be premature, if not downright irresponsible, to claim that it is presently established.

REFERENCES

1. American Psychological Association. Working Group on Investigation of Memories of Childhood Abuse—Final Conclusions. Washington, DC: American Psychological Association, Public Affairs Office, 1996.

2. Two classic papers on the fallibility of clinical observation, and the need for more systematic controlled research are: Chapman LJ, Chapman JP. Genesis of popular but erroneous diagnostic observations. J Abn Psychology 72:193-204, 1967; and Chapman LJ, Chapman JP. Illusory correlation as an obstacle to the use of valid psychodiagnostic signs. J Abn Psychology 74:271-280, 1969. These studies showed that even intelligent and well-trained clinicians reported "illusory correlations" between clearly invalid tests and clinical symptoms. These clinicians were not irresponsible; they were simply driven by *a priori* beliefs that could survive even clearly contradictory data.

3.   See: Ryan AJ. Anabolic steroids are fool's gold. Fed Proceedings 40:2682-2688, 1981.

4.   Haupt HA, Rovere GD. Anabolic steroids: A review of the literature. Am J Sports Med 12:469-484, 1984.

5.   See discussions of this issue in studies from our own laboratory: Pope HG Jr, Katz DL. Affective and psychotic syndromes associated with use of anabolic steroids. Am J Psychiatry 145:487-490, 1988; Pope HG Jr, Katz DL. Psychiatric and medical effects of anabolic-androgenic steroids: A controlled study of 160 athletes. Arch Gen Psychiatry 51:375-382, 1994; and Kouri E, Pope HG Jr, Katz DL, Oliva PS. Fat-free mass index in users and non-users of anabolic-androgenic steroids. Clin J Sport Med 5:223-228, 1995. For an example of a modern, properly designed, appropriately controlled study of the muscular gains produced by steroids, see: Bhasin S, Storer TW, Berman N, Callegari C, Clevenger B, Phillips J, et al. The effects of supraphysiologic doses of testosterone on muscle size and strength in normal men. N Engl J Med 335:1-7, 1996.

6.   Feingold BF. Hyperkinesis and learning disabilities linked to artificial food flavors and colors. Am J Nurs 75:797-803, 1975.

7.   Crook WG. Food allergy—The great masquerader. Pediatr Clin North Am 22:227-238, 1975.

8.   Bennett FC, Sherman R. Management of childhood "hyperactivity" by primary care physicians. J Dev Behav Pediatr 4:88-93, 1983.

9.   Milich R, Pelham WE. Effects of sugar ingestion on the classroom and playground behavior of attention deficit disordered boys. J Consult Clin Psychology 54:714-718, 1986.

10. Behar D, Rapoport JL, Adams AJ, Berg CJ, Cornblath M. Sugar challenge testing with children considered behaviorally "sugar reactive." Nutr Behav 1:277-288, 1984.

11. Wolraich ML, Lindgren SD, Stumbo PJ, Stegink LD, Applebaum MI, Kiritsy MC. Effects of diets high in sucrose or aspartame on the behavior and cognitive performance of children. New Engl J Med 330:301-307, 1994.

12. Kinsbourne M. Sugar and the hyperactive child. New Engl J Med 330:355-356, 1994.

Part Two:
Does Childhood Sexual Abuse Cause Adult Psychiatric Disorders?

12

CAR ACCIDENTS AND
BRAIN TUMORS

O UR INSPECTION OF SCIENTIFIC studies has shown us that the evidence for "repressed memories" is tenuous at best. We now turn to an equally heated debate: does sexual abuse in childhood cause psychiatric disorders in adulthood? Like "repression," this idea is often presented as an established fact, something so obvious that "everybody knows" it to be true. However, as illustrated by the next chapter on salt and high blood pressure, medicine is full of beliefs that "everybody knows," and which even esteemed professionals "know," but which may not be true at all. In the following chapters, we present some of the methodological flaws found in published studies that deal with childhood sexual abuse. We conclude, as we did for repression, that the jury is still out. We simply do not know whether childhood sexual abuse causes people to develop psychiatric disorders years later in adulthood.

Before starting this discussion, though, we must make clear what we are *not* saying. We are not disputing, for a moment, that childhood sexual abuse is common in our society, that it is morally repugnant, or that it should be condemned and punished whenever it occurs. We are not debating how often claims of childhood sexual abuse may be true or false, how often the so-called "false memory syndrome" may occur, or how many perpetrators may go unrecognized and unpunished. Important as these issues may be, they are tangential to the purely scientific question posed here about the relationship between childhood sexual abuse and adult psychiatric disorders.

An example will illustrate this point. There is no scientific evidence that car accidents cause people to develop malignant brain tumors. But despite this knowledge, we do not endorse or forgive car accidents, nor do we claim that perpetrators of car accidents should be exonerated. We are simply stating that if one is trying to understand the causes of brain cancer, it will be a great waste of time to meticulously interview brain cancer victims about their history of car accidents. Indeed, such a study would be a disservice to these victims, because it would direct scarce resources into an unrewarding channel. Better to save those resources for studies that might discover the true causes of brain tumors, and perhaps better treatments for them. There might even be some resources left over to help find better ways to reduce car accidents.

In short, the role of childhood sexual abuse in the causation of adult psychiatric disorders is an important question. It is not a political, moral, or ethical question, and it should not be miscast as such. It is a scientific question, a question with important practical implications for research and therapy. Having demarcated the question, then, how much can science legitimately claim to know?

13

Is Salt Actually
Bad for You?

QUESTIONABLE MEDICAL AND psychological be-
liefs can become so widely accepted in the general population,
and even among professionals themselves, that everyone begins
to accept them as axiomatic. We can become so indoctrinated
that we may even pass laws based on these beliefs, without stopping to question their validity.

A classic example of such a belief is the idea that salt restriction is highly effective for reducing blood pressure. Every day, we
see authoritative publications discussing salt consumption and the
sodium content of various foods; restaurants and supermarkets offer foods with reduced sodium; and even the United States Food
and Drug Administration has published reference values for daily
sodium intake. Indeed, by federal law, all foods sold in the United
States must be labeled with the amount of sodium per serving and
the percent of the daily reference value. Surely, then, it must be
firmly established scientifically that restriction of sodium intake is
helpful for reducing blood pressure.

But are we sure? Recently, a comprehensive statistical analysis of the research in this area was published in the *Journal of the American Medical Association* (1). The authors examined 56 studies, chosen according to rigorous criteria, and found that diastolic blood pressure (the lower of the two figures in a blood pressure reading, and the one that is more important in determining health risk) was not significantly affected by reducing sodium, either in people with high blood pressure or people with normal blood pressure. For example, looking at the 28 studies that examined individuals with normal blood pressure, sodium restriction reduced the diastolic pressure by an average of only 0.1 mm. In other words, for people with blood pressure of 120/80, the average diastolic pressure was reduced only to 79.9. And even this minute difference might be false, since the investigators were able to show that studies failing to find an effect of salt on blood pressure were probably less likely to have been published in the first place than were studies with a positive result. This phenomenon is called "publication bias," or, more colloquially, the "bottom drawer effect," referring to the fact that scientists may relegate their non-significant findings to the "bottom drawer" and not send them for publication. When we correct for the possible effects of publication bias in the literature on salt restriction and blood pressure, the effect of salt may vanish completely.

How, then, did we become so certain that salt was harmful? One reason may be that early studies, comparing the blood pressures of people in different countries, found that people who had less salt in their diets also displayed lower blood pressure. It turns out, however, when one controls these data for confounding variables, such as obesity and alcohol consumption, then salt consumption has very little effect on blood pressure at all. But despite these flaws, the findings of cross-cultural studies were quoted and re-quoted, until eventually everybody "knew" that salt was bad for health.

Medicine is full of such beliefs. We all "know," for example, that bad weather can exacerbate the pains of arthritis, or that eating chocolate can exacerbate acne. The problem is that neither of these beliefs is true. It is just that we have heard them so often that we have come to accept them as established facts. And these particular "facts" have all arisen in more "biological" branches of medicine. In psychiatry, we have far fewer definitive biological or physical methods to test the truth of hypotheses. Therefore, if unproven beliefs can take root so easily in general medicine, it stands to reason that such beliefs in psychiatry might proliferate even more wildly.

The lesson of all this is that we must be humble about how much we claim to know. Earlier authorities in psychology and psychiatry have made terrible mistakes because they lacked that humility. In past years, for example, numerous mothers were accused of having made their children schizophrenic, because of theories that bad mothering caused schizophrenia. These mothers suffered shame and guilt all of their lives unnecessarily—because it is now almost universally conceded that schizophrenia is caused by biological abnormalities. To cite another example, gay men in the past were treated with years of psychotherapy, and even with behavioral techniques using electric shocks, in an attempt to "cure" their homosexuality and make them heterosexual. Now it is widely admitted that homosexuality is a stable trait, unlikely to change with psychotherapy or "punishment" techniques. Indeed, the American Psychiatric Association no longer classifies ordinary homosexuality as an illness. Similarly, people with all manner of medical disorders, from asthma to ulcerative colitis to stomach ulcers, were once presumed to have "psychosomatic" illnesses, and were told that only psychotherapy could truly cure their conditions. Now we know that these conditions have a clear biological basis, and are not caused by mental problems. What other follies might contemporary psychologists and psychiatrists be endorsing at this very moment? Which of our current beliefs will seem foolish—if not downright harmful—when reviewed by the next generation?

One possibility for such a belief is the assumption that childhood sexual abuse causes people to develop psychiatric disorders in adulthood. Everybody "knows" that this is true, just as everybody "knows" that salt is bad for blood pressure. Even to question the malignant psychiatric effects of childhood sexual abuse is often considered heretical—just as it would have been almost scandalous, a generation ago, to question whether bad mothering could turn children into schizophrenics. Yet, the studies suggesting that childhood sexual abuse causes adult psychopathology suffer from a multitude of methodological problems that render their results almost uninterpretable. We will explain these methodological problems in detail in subsequent chapters, but it is worth introducing the terms here. The first of these problems is *selection bias*: individuals with a psychiatric disorder who also happen to have a history of childhood sexual abuse may be more likely to be included in study samples than individuals without such a history. Then there is *information bias*: the frequency with which subjects report a history of childhood sexual abuse may be biased by the subjects' knowledge that they do or do not suffer from psychiatric disorders. And the investigators interviewing the subjects may introduce further information bias in recording the subjects' reported histories. Finally, even if one could eliminate selection bias and information bias, there remains the massive problem of *confounding variables*. Specifically, individuals who have been sexually abused have also been subject to countless other events. They have often been victims of broken families, physical abuse, psychological neglect, and other adverse environmental influences. Also, they may have inherited psychiatric disorders from the very individuals in their families who abused them. Manic-depressive illness or alcohol dependence, for example, may provoke a perpetrator to engage in sexual abuse. But these disorders also have an established genetic component, and may be passed on to a child. If one removed all of these confounding variables, would childhood sexual abuse still show an effect on adult psychopathology? Or would its effects, like those of salt restriction on blood pressure, vanish into insignificance?

As we have stated above, the answer to this question matters a great deal. If childhood sexual abuse does cause adult psychiatric disorders, then many adult patients will require treatment focused on these experiences. If they fail to receive such treatment, they may not get better, or may show less improvement than they should. On the other hand, if we treat adult psychiatric disorders on the assumption that they are caused by childhood sexual abuse, and this theory turns out to be false, then we may be wasting enormous time and energy that might be better used for more effective treatments—much as some people with high blood pressure may be distracted from getting more effective treatment by their single-minded pursuit of salt restriction.

In a word, then, it is very important to scrutinize the scientific quality of studies that propose to assess whether childhood sexual abuse can cause adult psychiatric disorders. In the next three chapters, we examine the three big methodological problems, mentioned above, that confront such studies: selection bias, information bias, and confounding variables. Unfortunately, as we will see, lack of attention to these issues renders most of the available studies of childhood sexual abuse and adult psychiatric disorders practically valueless.

REFERENCES

1.   Midgley JP, Matthew AG, Greenwood CMT, Logan AG. Effect of reduced dietary sodium on blood pressure: A meta-analysis of randomized controlled trials. JAMA 275:1590-1597, 1996.

14

DOES SMOKING CAUSE ARTHRITIS?

HUNDREDS, IF NOT THOUSANDS, of simply designed studies have now appeared in the literature examining the prevalence of childhood sexual abuse in various populations of patients with psychiatric disorders. Here is an example of a hypothetical study of this type (1):

Drs. Harrison and James interviewed 50 women who were being treated for eating disorders at a clinic. Some of the women had bulimia nervosa, a disorder characterized by compulsive eating binges, followed by self-induced vomiting. Other women had anorexia nervosa; they had dieted until they weighed much less than they ought to weigh, but they still perceived themselves as too fat. Many of the women had experienced both disorders at various times over the years. For comparison, Drs. Harrison and James also interviewed 50 women of the same age who were recruited from the community at large. The community women were included only if they showed no evidence of a major psychiatric disorder. The investigators found that 25 (50%) of the 50 women with eating disorders reported a history of childhood sexual abuse, as compared to only 5 (10%) of the comparison women from the community. This difference proved to be highly "statistically significant." Specifically, using a statistical test, called Fisher's exact test, the investigators calculated that the odds of such a difference occurring by chance alone were less than 1 in 10,000. Thus, in the text of the paper, the authors added the phrase "$p < 0.0001$ by Fisher's exact test, two-tailed." On the basis of this highly significant finding, they concluded that childhood sexual abuse played an important causal role in the development of eating disorders.

Are the conclusions of this hypothetical study justified? The answer is no, for several reasons. First, our hypothetical investigators have failed to consider possible methodological errors in their design that might produce an apparent *association* between childhood sexual abuse and adult psychiatric disorders, even though a true association might not exist. Second, even if we allow for a true association between childhood sexual abuse and eating disorders, the investigators have still failed to demonstrate that the association is a *causal* association. In this chapter and the next, we consider flaws in our hypothetical study that might have caused the finding of a false association. In Chapter 16, we move on to the issue of causality.

The first possible cause of a false association in our hypothetical study—and in countless actual studies in the literature—is the problem of *selection bias*. Selection bias refers to the possibility that the investigators have selected subjects who are not representative of the overall population of such people in the world at large. A famous example of selection bias occurred in an election poll during the 1936 United States presidential campaign of Alfred Landon vs. Franklin Roosevelt. The poll predicted that

Landon would win easily, a prediction that turned out to be completely wrong. The problem was that the poll had used the telephone to solicit responses. People who could afford telephones were more likely to vote for Landon, whereas those without telephones were more likely to favor Roosevelt. Therefore, by using the telephone, the poll introduced a selection bias big enough to predict victory for the wrong candidate.

In the hypothetical study of Drs. Harrison and James, selection bias could appear in two places. First, the women coming to their clinic for treatment of eating disorders may have a higher or lower prevalence of childhood sexual abuse than women with eating disorders in the general population. Second, the comparison women recruited from the community may have a higher or lower incidence of sexual abuse than community women as a whole. Let us examine each of these possibilities.

First, are Drs. Harrison and James' subjects with eating disorders representative, in other words typical, of people with eating disorders as a whole? One can think of many reasons why they may not be. For example, women with eating disorders who also happen to have a history of childhood sexual abuse may be more inclined to seek psychological treatment than women with eating disorders who have no history of childhood trauma at all. Another possibility is that Drs. Harrison and James may be well known for their interest in childhood trauma. If so, then women with eating disorders who also happen to have a sexual abuse history may be somewhat more inclined to seek treatment at Harrison and James' clinic, whereas women without sexual abuse may be somewhat more likely to visit a different clinic across town.

For reasons such as these, the sample of women investigated by Drs. Harrison and James will probably show a higher prevalence of sexual abuse than women with eating disorders as a whole. But there is likely an equally serious reverse bias in the investigators' comparison group. Suppose we find that Drs. Harrison and James chose their comparison subjects by posting an advertisement around their local medical area seeking "women for a study involving interviews regarding their psychological symptoms" and offering them $30 to participate. Clearly, the women who are willing to respond to such an advertisement are not a random sample. In particular, women with a history of serious childhood sexual abuse may be embarrassed to sign up for a psychiatric interview. It is not worth $30 to them to have a stranger asking them about their childhood experiences. Thus, the women who actually show up in Drs. Harrison and James' offices, ready to be interviewed about their psychiatric histories, will likely exhibit a much lower rate of childhood sexual abuse than the true rate in the population.

Then, Drs. Harrison and James compound the problem even further with their requirement that these comparison subjects be free of psychiatric disorder. This criterion introduces a further selection bias into the comparison group, in that it creates a sample of "supernormals" who now have a much lower prevalence of psychiatric disorder as a whole than the baseline rate in the community.

What is so bad about using "supernormals?" Consider an analogy from medicine. Suppose that we wish to test the hypothesis that cigarette smoking causes people to develop rheumatoid arthritis. (This hypothesis, as the reader probably knows, is completely false.) We examine 50 patients with confirmed rheumatoid arthritis and obtain detailed histories of their lifetime cigarette consumption. We find that 50% report some history of cigarette use. We then get a comparison group of individuals from the community at large, choosing them so that their average age and male/female ratio match closely with the rheumatoid arthritis group, and exclude from this group any individuals who show evidence of any significant medical disease. In this group of "healthy controls," we find, not surprisingly, that the lifetime prevalence of cigarette smoking is markedly lower than in the patients with rheumatoid arthritis. Can we conclude, therefore, that smoking causes rheumatoid arthritis? Of course not. We have simply selected against cigarette smokers in the comparison group by our insistence that they be "supernormals" with no serious medical illness of any type.

How are Drs. Harrison and James to deal with these problems? Fortunately, these methodological difficulties are well understood in epidemiological research, and established methods exist to address them. For example, Drs. Harrison and James could obtain data from 1,000 women in the community at large. Upon examining the histories of these women, let us say that they find that 50 of the 1,000 women display eating disorders. These women are unselected, in that they represent every case of eating disorders in the sample, regardless of whether they were seeking treatment. Then, Drs. Harrison and James select from the remaining 950 women an age-matched group of 50 comparison subjects without regard to the presence or absence of psychiatric disorders (except, of course, an eating disorder). Assuming that all of the 50 subjects in each of the two groups agree to cooperate with the investigation (thus minimizing any bias from self-selection), Drs. Harrison and James will have two groups unlikely to be seriously affected by selection bias.

Although these methods are admittedly more tedious and expensive than the "quick and dirty" hypothetical study described earlier, it is easy to see that they would produce much more reliable results. It is remarkable, then, to find that the great majority of published studies of childhood sexual abuse and adult psychiatric disorder fail to control for selection bias, and thus may produce findings just as suspect as our bogus conclusion that smoking causes arthritis. In short, by insisting on studies that have adequately ad-

dressed the issue of selection bias, we have already greatly narrowed the field of studies which meet our methodological standards for testing the relationship between childhood sexual abuse
and adult psychiatric disorder.

REFERENCE

1.   This hypothetical study, and most of the material in this chapter, as well as
      Chapters 15, 16, and 19, are taken from a journal article which we have
      previously published: Pope HG Jr, Hudson JI. Does childhood sexual abuse
      cause adult psychiatric disorders? Essentials of methodology. J Psychiatry
      Law 363-381, Fall 1995. We refer the reader desiring a full scientific pres-
      entation of these arguments to the original article.

15

THE PREGNANT WOMEN
AND THE POWER LINES

L ET US SUPPOSE THAT Drs. Harrison and James, the hypothetical investigators in Chapter 14, have now received a large research grant. Using this money, they design a new and far superior study to avoid the problem of selection bias. They obtain 50 women with eating disorders and 50 comparison women from a large community sample in the manner previously described. In this new improved study, the difference in the prevalence of sexual abuse between the eating disordered subjects and the comparison group subjects has narrowed. Now, the doctors find that only 20 (40%) of the 50 women with eating disorders report a history of childhood sexual abuse as compared to 10 (20%) of the controls. The difference between groups in the prevalence of history of childhood sexual abuse is not nearly as robust as in the previous, more seriously biased design, but it is still statistically significant (it is now only $p < .05$ by Fisher's exact test, two-tailed). Can our investigators now conclude that sexual abuse has a causal role, albeit a more modest one, in eating disorders?

Unfortunately, they cannot, because they still have failed to deal with the equally serious potential problem of *information bias.* This form of bias refers to the error caused when the investigators obtain inaccurate information (for whatever reason) from subjects in one or both study samples, leading them to overestimate or underestimate the true prevalence of childhood sexual abuse in the groups.

How might such bias occur? To begin with, it can occur if the investigators are not blinded, meaning that they know whether they are interviewing a subject with an eating disorder or a comparison subject. When interviewing a subject with an eating disorder, an unblinded investigator may perhaps probe slightly more carefully, ask slightly more detailed questions about a history of childhood sexual abuse, than when interviewing a comparison subject. Such bias might be very subtle, and the investigator might introduce it quite unconsciously, yet it could slightly skew the responses of the eating-disordered women in favor of reporting a history of childhood sexual abuse and the responses of the comparison women against such reporting.

Of course, the investigators could deal with this problem by obtaining sexual abuse history while blinding themselves to the group status of the subject. In other words, one investigator could obtain the eating disorder history on the subject, and then present the subject to a second investigator who would inquire about sexual abuse history without any knowledge of whether the interviewee was an eating-disordered subject or a comparison subject. But this strategy does not completely resolve the problem of information bias, because even if the investigators are blinded, the subject herself is not. And she may be powerfully biased by a phenomenon known in psychology as *effort after meaning.*

Effort after meaning refers to the natural human tendency to seek an explanation for our suffering (1). For example, if one were to become severely depressed at this moment, one could easily construct a very plausible explanation of why the depression started now as opposed to 6 months ago or 6 months in the future. One tends to do this automatically, because it is difficult to accept that sheer bad fortune, or random acts of nature, can account for one's psychiatric problems. By analogy, it is likely that women with eating disorders (or patients with any sort of psychiatric disorder), in their effort after meaning, have carefully reflected about events in their past lives. They are likely to have thought about any traumatic or unusual situations that they endured, perhaps wondering if these traumas may have contributed to their current symptoms. Moreover, most patients cannot help but have been influenced by the traditional psychodynamic ("Freudian") belief that adverse childhood experiences lead to "neurotic" problems in adulthood. This belief is so ubiquitous in our society that it tends to steer patients to look particularly at their childhood in their effort after meaning. And more specifically, if patients have seen recent popular presentations in the media about the issue of childhood sexual abuse and psychiatric disorders, they might be particularly likely to have reflected carefully upon possible childhood abuse experiences, even relatively minor ones, in their history. If they have engaged in psychotherapy, they may have explored their history of childhood sexual abuse in detail with a therapist. By contrast, subjects with no psychiatric disorder may have devoted little thought to their childhood experiences, because they had no motivation to engage in an effort after meaning (2).

Effort after meaning produces a type of information bias known as *recall bias*, and this bias is frequently encountered throughout medicine. For example, suppose that we decide to study 50 mothers who have just given birth to infants with congenital malformations, and then interview a comparison group of 50 mothers whose infants were entirely normal. We ask both groups of mothers if they can remember having been in the vicinity of high tension power lines at any time during their pregnancy. It would not be surprising if the mothers of the malformed infants recalled a higher frequency of such exposure—not because their true exposure was any higher, but because these mothers had spent long and tortuous hours reflecting upon every possible adverse experience during their pregnancy that might possibly have caused their infants to become malformed. The mothers of the normal infants, on the other hand, would have devoted little thought to their experiences with power lines, even though their average level of exposure probably was about the same as that of the first group of women. Indeed, one recent study of mothers of malformed infants came out with just this sort of finding. These mothers correctly recalled various types of biological or chemical exposures that had actually been documented in their medical records, such as urinary tract or yeast infections, antibiotic drug use, and use of birth controls after conception, much more often than did a comparison group of mothers of normal infants (3).

Recall bias may occur for reasons other than effort after meaning. The astute reader may have already considered one other possibility. Suppose that, in spite of our skepticism in the first section of this book, repression of traumatic memories really does occur, and suppose further, as some theorists believe (see Chapter 1), that individuals with repressed memories of trauma are precisely those most likely to suffer its aftereffects. If all of this were true, then some patients with psychopathology might have amnesia for childhood sexual abuse that they had actually experienced—thus producing a recall bias in the opposite direction. While we might consider such a bias unlikely, some advocates of repression theory would argue that this bias would be substantial.

As can be seen, recall bias poses a serious problem for Drs. Harrison and James in their hypothetical study. Unlike the study of mothers just described, where one can check medical records to confirm various exposure factors, our investigators have little opportunity to confirm reports of childhood sexual abuse in their two groups of women. Indeed, the inability to confirm reports about the past is always and forever a problem in retrospective studies, as we have discussed earlier in Chapters 6 and 7 regarding retrospective studies of the repression hypothesis. The only definitive way to resolve the problem, as we have also discussed earlier, would be to do a prospective study. Such a design is proposed in Chapter 19.

REFERENCES

1. This phenomenon is discussed in Barlett FC. Remembering: A Study in Experimental and Social Psychology. Cambridge, UK: Cambridge Univ Press, 1932. See also: Tennant C. Life events and psychological morbidity: The evidence from prospective studies. Psychol Med 13:483-486, 1983.

2. Two contributory logical flaws that compound the problem here are the "representativeness heuristic" and "availability heuristic." The former error is the assumption that a causal inference is correct because it "feels right." Since childhood sexual abuse is universally recognized to be a terrible act, it "feels right" that it should have terrible consequences—even if the data to support this conclusion are not there. Under the "availability heuristic," easily available "explanations" come to mind and seem more plausible than less easily available ones. Given the attention accorded childhood sexual abuse in the contemporary media, a patient may be more willing to accept this "explanation" for his or her psychopathology than an explanation based on say, a deficit of serotonin transporter protein or some other more technical theory. For a discussion of these and other issues, see: Gilovich T. How We Know What Isn't So, cited in Chapter 7 of the first section.

3. Werler MM, Pober BR, Nelson K, Holmes LB. Reporting accuracy among mothers of malformed and nonmalformed infants. Am J Epidemiology 129:415-421, 1989.

16

Don't Buy That Lawrence
Welk Recording!

IN THE PREVIOUS TWO chapters, we have shown how selection bias and information bias seriously compromise virtually all retrospective studies. But let us suppose that our intrepid investigators, Drs. Harrison and James, have now received a still larger research grant to do an even more refined study. They obtain a huge community sample and select subjects with eating disorders and matched control subjects, taking great care to minimize selection bias. Then they interview subjects in both groups under blinded conditions to avoid any information bias introduced by the investigator. Instances of sexual abuse in both the eating-disordered and control group are scored only if the abuse is unequivocal and meets rigorous diagnostic criteria of demonstrated reliability. Further, let us suppose that the investigators are able to obtain confirmatory evidence in some manner to show that the sexual abuse actually did occur in the cases in which it is reported (this last item is probably a somewhat unrealistic expectation, but let us grant it for the purposes of discussion). Let us suppose that, even with all of these rigorous methods to control for bias, Drs. Harrison and James still are able to show a statistically significant difference when they compare the prevalence of sexual abuse in the subjects with eating disorders and the control subjects. Can they now, at last, conclude that childhood sexual abuse contributes to the development of eating disorders?

Unfortunately, they still cannot. We will now grant that they have shown an association between childhood sexual abuse and eating disorders. However, as we have stated earlier, the fact that there is an *association* between A and B does not necessarily mean that A *caused* B. In fact, logically, there are three alternative explanations for the association, as shown in the figure below:

1) A $\longrightarrow$ B

2) B $\longrightarrow$ A

3) A $\nwarrow$ $\nearrow$ B
     C

In examining this figure, let us assume that childhood sexual abuse is "A" and adult psychiatric disorder is "B." The first possibility, as the figure shows, is that A causes B. In this case, that would be the possibility that childhood sexual abuse causes adult psychiatric disorders. This of course is the hypothesis that we wish to test. But to establish this possibility, we must first rule out two other possibilities. First, we must consider the possibility that B causes A (i.e., that psychiatric disorder somehow predisposes a person to sexual abuse), and second, we must allow for the possibility that B and A do not cause one another, but are both caused by a third factor, C (which is often called a "confounding variable").

Let us look at these alternative possibilities. First, consider the possibility that B causes A. There are many examples of this type of association in ordinary life and in clinical medicine. Suppose, for example, that we interview 100 overweight subjects and ask them if they have a history of having used artificial sweeteners in their coffee at some time in the last year. We then pose the same question to 100 thin subjects. We find a highly significant difference showing a clear association between the use of artificial sweeteners and being overweight. Do we conclude, therefore, that artificial sweeteners cause obesity? Clearly not. The true direction of causality is that B causes A, namely that being overweight leads individuals to use artificial sweeteners more frequently.

More difficult and less trivial examples come from clinical medicine. Thirty years ago, for example, a study found that physically active agricultural workers were less likely to develop heart disease than sedentary agricultural workers (1). Would it be correct to conclude, therefore, that being sedentary contributes to the evolution of heart disease? No. We must allow for the alternative possibility that workers who already had early symptoms of incipient heart disease (e.g., chest pain on exertion) would be more likely to choose sedentary agricultural jobs than their counterparts who had no symptoms of evolving cardiac disease. In other words, B may have led to A, rather than A to B.

Another obvious example exists in the area of sexual abuse: individuals with mental retardation are more likely to have experienced sexual abuse than individuals of normal intelligence (2). But clearly it would be illogical to conclude that childhood sexual abuse causes mental retardation. Rather, mentally retarded individuals are more at risk for victimization because they are less able to defend themselves against abuse.

But do these arguments extend to adult psychiatric disorders? Is it reasonable to argue that bulimia nervosa, depressive illness, or anxiety disorders, appearing in an individual at the age of 20, could possibly have predisposed him or her to have been sexually abused at the age of 8? This possibility is not as far fetched as it might seem. Specifically, studies have shown that individuals with adult psychiatric disorders have often experienced prodromal symptoms (in other words, premonitory symptoms) of their disorders extending far back into childhood. For example, adults who display panic disorder or bulimia nervosa are more likely to have experienced fear of going to school ("school phobia"), fear of being separated from their mothers ("separation anxiety"), or bedwetting ("primary enuresis") in childhood (3). Similarly, individuals with eating disorders as adults often have histories of depressive or anxiety disorders long prior to the onset of the eating disorder (4). Therefore, it is possible that some individuals with eating disorders in Harrison and James' study may have displayed a degree of depression or other psychological distress, even years ago in childhood, that rendered them more vulnerable to being preyed upon by potential abusers.

Admittedly, this particular direction of causality might account for only a small portion of the possible association between childhood sexual abuse and adult psychiatric disorders. However, we still have to rule out the last of the possibilities shown in the figure on page 102, namely that A and B are both caused by a confounding variable, C. The issue of confounding is again a constant problem, both in ordinary life and in clinical medicine. To begin with a simple example, suppose that we were to study 100 residents of a nursing home and ask them if they had ever purchased a Lawrence Welk recording. Lawrence Welk was a famous band leader whose recordings were very popular several decades ago. Therefore, we would likely find that a high percentage of the nursing home residents reported that they had bought at least one such a recording at some time. If we then obtained a comparison group from the community at large, we would undoubtedly find that a far smaller percentage of our comparison subjects had made such a purchase. In fact, some of them would probably report that they had never even heard of Lawrence Welk. Does it follow from our findings that buying a Lawrence Welk recording will cause you to end up in a nursing home? Should we put warning stickers on all Lawrence Welk recordings in record stores, alerting potential purchasers to the risk? Clearly not. In fact, the association between ownership of Lawrence Welk recordings and nursing home residence is simply attributable to the confounding variable of advanced age. In other words, age is the "C" on page 102.

Turning to medicine, the literature is filled with discredited theories that failed to take into account the possibility of confounding variables. Even elegant and expensive studies, involving big teams of investigators and hundreds of thousands of dollars in costs, have sometimes proved dead wrong when it was later discovered that a confounding variable had created a mere illusion of causality. Of the many examples that could be cited, one was the finding of an association between the use of inhaled nitrites (so-called "poppers") and the development of AIDS (5). In the early 1980s, before the human immunodeficiency virus (HIV) had been isolated, various epidemiologic studies were conducted to assess what factors might cause people to develop AIDS. It was found that homosexual men who used "poppers" to get a "rush" during sexual activity were markedly more likely to develop AIDS than homosexual men who had not used these drugs. Some studies even conducted elaborate statistical tests, called regression analyses (to be discussed in more detail in the next chapter), in an attempt to rule out possible confounding variables. Nevertheless, inhaled nitrites still emerged as a statistically significant factor, and it was concluded that they might cause, or at least contribute to, the development of AIDS.

Now, of course, we know that nitrites do not cause AIDS, and that the disease is instead caused simply by infection with a specific virus, HIV. It turns out, in retrospect, that certain sexual practices that predispose people to HIV transmission (especially receptive anal intercourse) are closely associated with the use of "poppers." In other words, the association between nitrite use and AIDS was a real one, but it was not a *causal* association at all. Instead, the association was caused by the presence of a confounding variable, namely specific sexual practices.

Returning, then, to the new hypothetical study by Drs. Harrison and James, we see that an association between childhood sexual abuse and adult psychiatric disorder, however rigorously proved, might not be a causal association at all. It might simply be due to any number of confounding variables. Individuals who have been sexually abused in childhood are also likely to have been physically abused, neglected, or subjected to all manner of other difficulties while growing up. Even more importantly, there may have been a genetic loading in their families for disorders such as alcohol dependence or manic-depressive illness (6). Relatives with alcoholism or manic episodes (the "high" periods of manic-depressive illness), in turn, may be more likely to abuse a child in the family. But that abuse victim already carries the genetic predisposition to develop psychopathology, even if he or she were not sexually abused. In other words, childhood sexual abuse and psychopathology would be expected to "travel together" down the family tree as a result of the confounding variable of genetics alone, even if the sexual abuse did not itself cause psychiatric disorders.

Data to support this speculation comes from one recent study that described 12 sexually abused women with bulimia nervosa (7). This study was one of the few in which the psychiatric diagnosis of the perpetrator, as well as that of the victim, was assessed. Of the 8 women in this study found to have been abused by a biological relative, 6 (75%) were abused by a family member diagnosed with alcohol dependence, a major mood disorder (such as manic-depressive illness), or both. Now, there is substantial evidence that alcoholism and major mood disorders are more prevalent in the family trees of individuals with bulimia nervosa than in the population at large, raising the possibility that there is a genetic link among these various disorders (8). It is possible, therefore, that genetic factors alone might account for the association of sexual abuse and bulimia nervosa observed in this investigation, and that sexual abuse itself had no role in *causing* the adult eating disorder.

In summary, association does not prove causality. This is not a difficult concept. It represents one of the most basic teachings of "Psychology 101." And it is easy to illustrate, as shown by our examples of the association between the use of artificial sweeteners and obesity, or the purchase of a Lawrence Welk recording and nursing home residence. Yet this elementary principle is ignored, or only barely acknowledged, in many scientific studies of childhood sexual abuse. It is even more rarely noted in popular reports of these studies in the media. The lay reader, hearing the latest media report of a new "major study" like that of Drs. Harrison and James, must be wary. A history of childhood sexual abuse may well be associated with some adult psychiatric disorders, but it is premature to jump from this finding to an assumption of causality.

REFERENCES

1. McDonough JR, Hames CG, Stulb SC, Garrison GE. Coronary heart disease among Negroes and Whites in Evans County, Georgia. J Chron Dis 18:443-468, 1965.

2. See: Tharinger D, Horton CB, Millea S. Sexual abuse and exploitation of children and adults with mental retardation. Child Abuse Negl 14:301-312, 1990; and Stromsness MM. Sexually abused women with mental retardation: Hidden victims, absent resources. Women and Therapy 14:139-152, 1993.

3.   See: Robinson PH, Holden NL. Bulimia nervosa in the male. Psychol Med 16:795-803, 1986; and Perugi G, Deltito J, Soriani A, Musetti L, Petracca A, Nisita C, et al. Relationships between panic disorder and separation anxiety with school phobia. Compr Psychiatry 29:98-107, 1988.

4.   See: Hudson JI, Pope HG Jr, Yurgelun-Todd D, Jonas JM, Frankenburg FR. A controlled study of lifetime prevalence of affective and other psychiatric disorders in bulimic outpatients. Am J Psychiatry 144:1283-1287, 1987; and Brewerton TD, Lydiard RB, Herzog DB, Brotman AW, O'Neil PM, Ballenger JC. Comorbidity of axis I psychiatric disorders. J Clin Psychiatry 56:77-80, 1995.

5.   For a discussion of how an association was erroneously assumed to be causal in this case, see: Vandenbroucke JP, Pardoel VP. An autopsy of epidemiologic methods: The case of "poppers" in the early epidemic of the acquired immunodeficiency syndrome. Am J Epidemiol 129:455-457, 1989.

6.   For reviews of genetic studies of these disorders, see: Cadoret RJ. Genetics of alcoholism. In Collins RL, Leonard KE, Searles JS, eds. Alcohol and the Family: Research and Clinical Perspectives. New York: Guildford Press, 1990; and Tsuang MT, Faraone SV. The Genetics of Mood Disorders. Baltimore: Johns Hopkins Univ Press, 1990.

7.   Bulik CM, Sullivan PF, Rorty M. Childhood sexual abuse in women with bulimia. J Clin Psychiatry 50:460-464, 1989.

8.   Hudson JI, Pope HG Jr. Affective spectrum disorder: Does antidepressant response identify a family of disorders with a common pathophysiology? Am J Psychiatry 147:552-564, 1990.

17

Alcohol Consumption, Lung Cancer, and Higher Mathematics

AS ILLUSTRATED BY THE experiences of our apocryphal investigators in the previous three chapters, the problems of selection bias, information bias, and confounding variables seriously compromise the conclusions of virtually all published studies examining the relationship between childhood sexual abuse and adult psychiatric disorders. As these flaws are more widely acknowledged, newer and more sophisticated studies are attempting to address the question of causality. Are these newer efforts helping us to reach a more definite answer?

Consider one recent study in the prestigious *American Journal of Public Health* (1). The authors examined survey responses from 1,099 randomly selected American women regarding their experiences of childhood sexual abuse and history of bulimic behaviors. The methodology was careful and sophisticated. The women were administered face-to-face structured interviews in which they were asked detailed questions. Specified operational diagnostic criteria were used both for the diagnosis of bulimic behaviors and for childhood sexual abuse. These strategies would be expected to minimize the problems of selection bias and information bias, discussed in our previous chapters. When the investigators analyzed the results of the study, they found that, even with these biases controlled, a clear association between bulimic behaviors and childhood sexual abuse still remained. In fact, binge-eating was twice as common among abused respondents as compared to non-abused respondents, and a full bulimic syndrome (binge-eating; overconcern about body weight; and a history of vomiting, laxative abuse, or similar measures) was three times as common in abused as opposed to non-abused women.

So much for association. But is the association *causal*? Or are bulimic behaviors and sexual abuse mutually caused by confounding variables? To deal with this question, the authors used a sophisticated mathematical technique called regression analysis, in which they calculated the "population attributable risk," or AR_c, where

$$AR_c = (x-y)/x$$

and where y, in turn, is defined by the formula

$$y = \sum_j n_j \hat{I}_j{}^*$$

Without stopping to explain all of these symbols (they are defined in the study), suffice it to say that even after mathematically controlling for the effects of age, ethnic group, and parents' educational level, the authors found that bulimic behavior was still associated with childhood sexual abuse. Specifically, the authors suggest that among the women with the full bulimic syndrome just described, as many as 34% of the cases would not have occurred in the absence of childhood sexual abuse.

Certainly this analysis represents an elegant mathematical treatment, far more sophisticated than the simplistic designs of Drs. Harrison and James in the preceding chapters. Do these findings now finally allow us to conclude that childhood sexual abuse causes bulimic behaviors, at least in some cases?

In our opinion, absolutely not. Consider again an example from medicine. Suppose that we surveyed 10,000 patients for their history of alcohol consumption and lung cancer, using the same survey and interviewing techniques described in the study above. We would find an association between alcohol and lung cancer. But is this a causal association? As it turns out, it is not. Alcohol in itself has little or no role in causing lung cancer. But people who drink alcohol also smoke more cigarettes, and cigarettes really do cause lung cancer. The confounding variable, in other words, is tobacco consumption.

Now suppose that we do a logistic regression analysis, just as in the bulimia study described above, and calculate "adjusted odds ratios" to measure the contribution of alcohol to lung cancer. As with the above bulimia study, we control for numerous variables, such as age, ethnic group, and parents' level of education. We even go further and control for additional variables: the respondents' height, weight, and blood pressure; their religious affiliation; political persuasion; and even their favorite brand of breakfast cereal. But we *still forget to control for their consumption of cigarettes.* What happens? We have used a lot more computer time, and our mathematics looks even fancier, but our findings continue to give the erroneous impression that alcohol is the culprit. We have still missed the real cause of lung cancer.

Now it may still be correct, in a certain technical sense, to say that alcohol is a "risk factor" for lung cancer, because people who drink *do* show a higher rate of lung cancer. And we could blur the whole issue a bit by arguing that alcohol is part of a "multifactorial group of interacting etiological factors" in lung cancer, or that it is part of an "integrated causal model" for lung cancer. All of this would sound very impressive if we did not know the simple truth. Alcohol doesn't cause lung cancer. Cigarettes do.

Returning then to the bulimia study reviewed here, we must acknowledge that its methods represent a considerable advance over most of the studies previously published in this area. Despite its sophistication, however, it still ultimately founders on the issue of confounding variables. Perhaps childhood sexual abuse *is* one of several related factors in the cause of bulimia nervosa, but these results still do not permit us to conclude that it necessarily has any causal role at all.

REFERENCE

1. Wonderlich SA, Wilsnack RW, Wilsnack SC, Harris TR. Childhood sexual abuse and bulimic behavior in a nationally representative sample. Am J Public Health 86:1082-1086, 1996.

18

WILL MASTURBATION SHRINK YOUR HIPPOCAMPUS?

SOPHISTICATED MATHEMATICAL techniques, such as those of the study described in the previous chapter, are not the only sort of "high technology" that has been brought to bear on the question of childhood sexual abuse and adult psychiatric disorders. Other scientists have used state-of-the-art techniques of neuroimaging. For example, the October 1995 issue of *Scientific American* mentions two recent studies that found that one region of the brain, called the left hippocampus, was smaller in victims of childhood sexual abuse than in comparison subjects (1). Does this mean that childhood sexual abuse leaves a measurable "mark" on the brain?

There is something elegant and satisfying about a study that shows a visible, measurable effect, such as a difference in brain structure as determined by computer-assisted imaging techniques. And it is particularly interesting to find differences in the hippocampus, because this area of the brain, as we have mentioned earlier, is involved with memory and emotions. But again, as we have illustrated in Chapter 3, we must not allow the "high tech" aspects of such studies to distract us from a careful examination of possible methodological weaknesses. One common weakness is the failure to use a properly matched comparison group. In particular, the subjects in the comparison group must be chosen so that they exhibit the same levels of psychiatric symptoms as the patients in the sexual abuse group, except for the fact that the comparison subjects were not sexually abused. If we fail to match in this manner, and instead use psychiatrically normal comparison subjects, then the abuse victims will of course differ from the comparison subjects in countless ways. But these differences may be simply nonspecific phenomena associated with overall psychiatric illness, and may have nothing to do with having been traumatized at all. Therefore, if we attributed our findings to the effects of sexual abuse, we would be in error.

To illustrate this problem, suppose that we were to go back many decades to the era when it was widely believed that excessive masturbation could cause mental problems, perhaps even insanity. We find a practitioner of that day, and ask him to give us a sample of 20 of his patients whom he has diagnosed as suffering from masturbation-induced mental illness. He provides us with 20 individuals, many of whom display prominent depression, anxiety, and other symptoms. We then recruit a comparison group of 20 age- and sex-matched individuals who show no evidence of mental disorders. We move our two groups forward to modern times, and compare them using a battery of state-of-the-art laboratory measurement techniques. We will probably find numerous statistically significant differences. For example, the patients with "masturbation-induced illness" will likely show higher scores on neuropsychological measures of their ability to pay attention and their short-term memory. They will probably show neuroendocrine abnormalities, such as higher cortisol levels, or changes in other hormones from the pituitary gland or the hypothalamus in the brain. They may even have smaller hippocampi. Can we now conclude that masturbation leaves a scar on the central nervous system? Clearly, this conclusion would not be logical. We have merely shown that a group of people selected because they were ill differ from a group of people selected because they were well. We cannot logically extrapolate from this observation to say that masturbation caused the abnormalities that we have observed.

By analogy, it appears that most present studies of victims of childhood sexual abuse, even those using technologically advanced measurement techniques, have demonstrated only that people with psychiatric illness show more abnormalities than people without psychiatric illness. Whether childhood sexual abuse or other traumas actually cause any of these abnormalities remains unclear.

Methods are available, however, to design a study by which one could more accurately address the question of whether childhood sexual abuse leaves a mark on the brain. For example, one could locate a group of patients who had been evaluated at a hospital and documented to be victims of childhood sexual abuse on the basis of medical examinations. Then, one would obtain from the same hospital a matched comparison group of subjects who were seen for some other reason, but who displayed no known history of childhood sexual abuse. By "matched," we mean that the comparison individuals would be of the same age, sex, and socioeconomic class as the abused group, and that they would display the same rates of current psychopathology, similar rates of psychiatric disorder in their family trees, and similar rates of adverse experiences in their childhood as the first group—except, of course, for sexual abuse. One could then compare these two groups on all manner of neuropsychological, neuroendocrine, and neuroanatomical measures. If the group with childhood sexual abuse displayed a given abnormality significantly more often than the otherwise matched control group, then—and only then—would we have compelling evidence that childhood sexual abuse leads to a measurable abnormality later on in the adult brain.

If this sounds like a difficult and expensive study, it is. But only with a rigorous scientific design like this would it be possible to state with reasonable confidence that childhood sexual abuse produces lasting abnormalities. Pending studies with such scrupulous methodology, we must remain skeptical of any statements that we hear about the long-term effects of sexual abuse on brain structure, hormone levels, or other biological findings.

REFERENCES

1. Mukerjee M. Hidden scars: Sexual and other abuse may alter a brain region. Scientific American 273 (4):14-20, 1995.

19

A METHODOLOGICALLY SOUND STUDY

THE PRECEDING CHAPTERS have presented a skeptical view of published studies proposing that childhood sexual abuse causes adult psychiatric disorders. In case after case, we have found flaws with the studies' methodology. Are we being too cynical? Are we proposing impossibly high standards? Do we have an "agenda" to discredit any study that seems to show that childhood sexual abuse does produce such effects?

Not at all. Indeed, it would be relatively straightforward (albeit expensive) to design a study of childhood sexual abuse and adult psychiatric disorders that would quickly answer all of the criticisms we have raised in the previous chapters. We have already sketched, at the end of chapter 18, what such a study would look like. It would be a prospective study, as contrasted with the retrospective designs used by virtually all of the sexual abuse studies described up to this point. The investigators in the study would obtain one group of subjects who were documented at some social service agency or hospital as victims of childhood sexual abuse. Then, they would take a comparison group of children, carefully matched in every way, except for the fact that they were not sexually abused. For example, they could take children who had been seen at the same hospital or social service agency as the sexual abuse group. Other matching factors would include the same degree of family psychopathology (similar rates of alcohol and drug abuse, major mood disorders, and other illnesses in the family tree), family environment (same prevalence of poor socioeconomic conditions, marital discord, family dysfunction, and neglect), and other variables—save for the fact that the comparison subjects were *not* victims of sexual abuse. The investigators would then follow these two matched groups of children longitudinally for a period of time and assess at a later date (preferably using blinded raters) whether the sexually abused group developed a higher prevalence of psychopathology as adults than did the otherwise matched control group. (They could also, of course, take advantage of this study design to see whether any of the sexual abuse victims repressed the memory of their trauma.) If the former group, differing from the controls only on the presence of sexual abuse, nevertheless displayed a higher rate of psychopathology, then one would have convincing evidence that childhood sexual abuse indeed contributes to adult psychiatric disorders (1).

Admittedly, such a study would be time consuming. One would need an experienced team of investigators over a period of time and ample funding to do the work properly. Some compromises could be made, however, to simplify the investigation, with only a modest sacrifice of methodological rigor. For example, one could examine a group of 100 individuals who were known from hospital or social service records to have been sexually abused many years ago, and then locate a matched group of individuals who had been seen at the same time for, say, medical evaluations.

However, this comparison group would have to be carefully matched (or, using a statistical technique, "stratified") so that the two groups would be comparable in terms of prevalence of familial psychiatric disorder, adverse familial and childhood environments, and all other possible confounding variables. For example, if it were found that many of the sexually abused children in this study came from homes with a single parent, with an alcoholic stepfather, a family history of anxiety disorders, and significant poverty, then one would have to find comparison subjects who had also suffered from these same familial influences, except for the fact that they were not sexually abused. Only by such a technique could the role of sexual abuse be properly isolated from other confounding variables, so that its effect could be evaluated in its own right.

Even though less expensive, this "partially retrospective-partially prospective" design would still cost a lot of money. But if we are serious about assessing the effects of sexual abuse, studies of this type must be performed, in spite of their cost. Millions upon millions of dollars have been spent assessing the role of cholesterol in heart disease; the long-term effects of hypertension on life expectancy; and the long-term health effects of diet, alcohol, cigarettes, and exposure to environmental and industrial substances. We have learned a great deal about all of these things, and, in the course of such research, dispelled many false beliefs that had arisen from earlier, less refined studies. It is time to admit that we are in a similar, early stage of knowledge regarding the effects of childhood sexual abuse. The proper methodology is available. It remains only for someone to do the necessary studies. Until then, however, it would not be appropriate to claim that childhood sexual abuse has been shown to cause adult psychiatric disorders (2).

REFERENCES

1. One of the few published studies to approach this level of methodologic quality is: Widom CS, Ames MA. Criminal consequences of childhood sexual victimization. Child Abuse Negl 18:303-318, 1994. These investigators prospectively examined the arrest records of several groups of adults. One group of 125 was documented from court records to have been sexually abused but not physically abused or neglected; another group of 609 had been neglected, but not sexually or physically abused; and a comparison group of 667 had no history of abuse at all. Looking at 12 different categories of arrest rates in adolescence and adulthood, including alcohol problems, drug abuse, and violence, the sexually abused group displayed *lower* rates on all 12 measures than the group that was only neglected. Indeed, the sexually abused group was lower on 6 of the 12 measures even when compared to the group that had not been abused in any way at all.

2. A federal report, prepared for the United States House of Representatives, has just appeared, examining the slightly narrower question of whether childhood sexual abuse causes individuals to become abusers themselves as adults. The report discusses virtually all of the same methodological flaws of available studies that we have discussed here—and concludes that the relationship between childhood sexual abuse and becoming an adult abuser is not established. The complete report is available as: U.S. General Accounting Office. Cycle of Sexual Abuse: Research Inconclusive about Whether Child Victims Become Adult Abusers. Report to the Chairman, Subcommittee on Crime, Committee on the Judiciary, House of Representatives. Washington, DC: GAO/GGD-96-178, Cycle of Sexual Abuse Research Results, September 1996.

FURTHER READING

I. Work from our laboratory:

Over the last several years, we have published a number of scientific articles looking at the issues of repression and childhood trauma. Many other articles are on the way, either in preparation or submitted for publication to various journals. The following list shows articles that have actually been published at the time of this writing. Copies of these articles may be obtained by calling the Biological Psychiatry Laboratory at (800) 444-0601, or writing to us at McLean Hospital, Belmont, Massachusetts, 02178.

Original Reports in Peer-Reviewed Journals:

Pope HG Jr, Hudson JI. Is childhood sexual abuse a risk factor for bulimia nervosa? Am J Psychiatry 149:455-463, 1992.

Pope HG Jr, Mangweth B, Negrão AB, Hudson JI, Cordás TA. Childhood sexual abuse and bulimia nervosa: A comparison of American, Austrian, and Brazilian women. Am J Psychiatry 151:732-737, 1994.

Lipinski JF, Pope HG Jr. Do flashbacks represent obsessive-compulsive imagery? Compr Psychiatry 35:245-247, 1994.

Pope HG Jr, Hudson JI. Can memories of childhood sexual abuse be repressed? Psychol Med 25:121-126, 1995.

Hudson JI, Pope HG Jr. Does childhood sexual abuse cause fibromyalgia? Arthritis Rheum 38:161-163, 1995.

Pope HG Jr, Hudson JI. Does childhood sexual abuse cause adult psychiatric disorders? Essentials of methodology. J Psychiatry Law 363-381,
Fall 1995.

Pope HG Jr, Hudson JI. "Recovered memory" therapy for eating disorders:
Implications of the Ramona verdict. Int J Eating Disord 19:139-145, 1996.

Other Publications of Interest:

Pope HG Jr, Hudson JI. Childhood sexual abuse and bulimia nervosa: Is
there an association? American Anorexia/Bulimia Association Newsletter, Special Research Edition, p. 6, Fall 1992.

Pope HG Jr, Hudson JI. Is childhood sexual abuse a risk factor for bulimia nervosa? (letter) Am J Psychiatry 150:357-358, 1993.

Pope HG Jr. "Recovered memories": Recent events and review of evidence. Currents in Affective Illness 13:5-12, 1994.

Pope HG Jr, Hudson JI. Can individuals "repress" memories of childhood
sexual abuse? An examination of the evidence. Psychiatric Annals
25:715-719, 1995.

II. WORK FROM OTHER CENTERS:

Many articles have now appeared, often in prestigious scientific journals, questioning the validity of the notion of repression
and/or the role of childhood trauma in causing adult psychopathology. Among these are:

Boakes J. False memory syndrome. Lancet 346:1048-1049, 1995.

Campbell TW. Repressed memories and statutes of limitations: Examining the data and weighing the consequences. Am J Forensic Psychiatry
16:25-51, 1995.

Frankel FH. Adult reconstruction of childhood events in the multiple personality literature. Am J Psychiatry 150:954-958, 1993.

Frankel FH. Discovering new memories in psychotherapy—Childhood
revisited, fantasy, or both? New Engl J Med 333:591-594, 1995.

Holmes D. The evidence for repression: An examination of sixty years of research. In Singer J, ed. Repression and Dissociation—Implications for Personality, Theory, Psychopathology and Health. Chicago: Univ of Chicago Press, 1990. See pp. 85-102.

Kihlstrom JF. Exhumed memory. In Lynn SJ, Spanos NP, eds. Truth in Memory. New York: Guilford Press. In press.

Lindsay DS, Read JD. "Memory work" and recovered memories of childhood sexual abuse: Scientific evidence and public, professional, and personal issues. Psychology Public Policy Law 1:846-908, 1995.

Loftus E. The reality of repressed memories. Am Psychologist 48:518-537, 1993.

Loftus EF, Pickrell JE. The formation of false memories. Psychiatric Annals 25:720-725, 1995.

McHugh PR. Psychiatric misadventures. Am Scholar 497-510, Autumn 1992.

McHugh PR. Psychotherapy awry. Am Scholar 17-30, Winter 1994.

McElroy SL, Keck PE. Recovered memory therapy: False memory syndrome and other complications. Psychiatric Annals 25:731-735, 1995.

Merskey H. Ethical issues in the search for repressed memories. Am J Psychotherapy 50:323-335, 1996.

Ofshe RJ, Singer MT. Recovered-memory therapy and robust repression: Influence and pseudomemories. Int J Clin Exp Hypn 42:391-410, 1994.

Paris J. A critical review of recovered memories in psychotherapy: Part I—Trauma and memory, and Part II—Trauma and therapy. Can J Psychiatry 41:201-210, 1996.

Schacter DK, Curran T. The cognitive neuroscience of false memories. Psychiatric Annals 25:726-730, 1995.

III. POPULAR WORKS:

Several excellent books have appeared reviewing the topics of repression and childhood trauma in terms more accessible to the lay reader. These include:

Campbell TW. Beware the Talking Cure: Psychotherapy May Be Hazardous to Your Mental Health. Boca Raton, FL: Upton Books, 1994.

Crews F. The Memory Wars: Freud's Legacy in Dispute. New York: New York Review of Books, 1995.

Dawes RM. House of Cards: Psychology and Psychotherapy Built on Myth. New York: Free Press, 1994.

Hagen MA. Whores of the Court: The Fraud of Psychiatric Testimony and the Rape of American Justice. New York: Regan Books, 1997.

Loftus E, Ketcham K. The Myth of Repressed Memory: False Memories and Allegations of Sexual Abuse. New York: St. Martins, 1994.

Ofshe RJ, Waters E. Making Monsters: False Memories, Psychotherapy and Sexual Hysteria. New York: Scribners, 1994.

Pendergrast M. Victims of Memory: Sex Abuse Accusations and Shattered Lives. 2d ed. Hinesburg, VT: Upper Access, Inc., 1996.

Underwager R, Wakefield H. The Return of the Furies: Analysis of Recovered Memory Therapy. Chicago: Open Court, 1994.

Wright L. Remembering Satan: A Case of Recovered Memory and the Shattering of an American Family. New York: Knopf, 1994.

Yapko MD. Suggestions of Abuse: True and False Memories of Childhood Sexual Traumas. New York: Simon & Schuster, 1994.

IV. How to evaluate a scientific study:

There are many good textbooks which discuss how to evaluate the methodological quality of scientific studies. Two examples are:

Hennekens CH, Buring JE. Epidemiology in Medicine. Boston: Little, Brown & Co., 1987.

Rothman KJ. Modern Epidemiology. Boston: Little, Brown & Co., 1986.

A couple of books for the lay reader also provide lucid discussions and colorful examples of how logic can go awry in both scientific studies and everyday life:

Nisbett R, Ross L. Human Inference: Strategies and Shortcomings of Social Judgement. Englewood Cliffs, NJ: Prentice-Hall, 1980.

Gilovich T. How We Know What Isn't So: The Fallability of Human Reason in Everyday Life. New York: The Free Press, 1991.

V. THE OPPOSING POSITION:

Among the various popular and scientific works arguing in favor of the "repression" theory, are:

Bass E, Davis L. The Courage to Heal: A Guide for Women Survivors of Child Sexual Abuse. 3d ed. New York: Harper Perennial, 1994.

Blume ES. Secret Survivors: Uncovering Incest and Its Aftereffects in Women. New York: Ballantine, 1990.

Fredrickson R. Repressed Memories: Journey to Recovery from Sexual Abuse. New York: Fireside/Parkside, S&S, 1992.

Freyd JJ. Betrayal Trauma: The Logic of Forgetting Childhood Abuse. Cambridge: Harvard Univ Press, 1996.

Herman JL. Trauma and Recovery. New York: Basic Books, 1992.

Pope KS. Memory, abuse, and science: Questioning claims about the false memory syndrome epidemic. Am Psychologist 51:957-974, 1996.

Terr L. Unchained Memories: True Stories of Traumatic Memories, Lost and Found. New York: Basic Books, 1994.

van der Kolk BA. The body keeps the score: Memory and the evolving psychobiology of posttraumatic stress. Harvard Rev Psychiatry 253-265, Jan/Feb 1994.

van der Kolk BA. Psychological Trauma. Washington, DC: American Psychiatric Press, 1987.

Whitfield CL. Memory and Abuse: Remembering and Healing the Effects of Trauma. Deerfield Beach, FL: Health Communications, Inc., 1995.

INDEX

ADHD (Child behavior disorder).
  See Attention-deficit hyperactivity disorder
AIDS (Disease), 45-46, 105-106
Alcoholism, 106-107
American Journal of Psychiatry, 31
American Journal of Public Health, 109
American Psychiatric Association, 4-5, 85
American Psychological Association, 73
Amnesia, 4
  and early childhood, 40, 48-49, 58-59, 65, 69
  dissociative, 5
  due to biological/neurological causes, 6, 19, 48-50
  in literature, 10-14
  psychogenic, 5-6
  traumatic, 5-6, 26-28, 37-39, 49-50, 98
Anorexia nervosa, 89
Association of attributes, 90, 102-107, 110-111
Attention-deficit hyperactivity disorder, 76
Beliefs, 33, 81, 83, 85-86, 97, 119
Bias, 43, 91, 95-96
  information, 86-87, 96-97, 101, 109-110
  publication, 84

recall, 97-98
response, 62, 66-70
selection, 86-87, 90-94, 95, 101-102, 109-110
Blood pressure, 81, 83-84, 86-87, 111
Brain, 3-6, 17-18, 25, 81-82
  and intelligence, 20
  and memory, 17-22
  and neuropsychological studies and testing, 17, 19, 22, 37, 114-115
  chemistry, 17-18
  research, 113, 115-116
Bulimia nervosa, 89, 103-104, 106-107, 109-112
Captains Courageous (Kipling), 13-14
Causality, 90, 102-107, 109-112
Childhood sexual abuse
  and adult psychiatric disorders, 4-5, 21, 81-82, 86-87, 89-90, 92-94, 97, 102-104, 106-107, 109, 113-115, 117-119
  and eating disorders, 89-91, 93, 95-97, 101-102, 104, 107, 109-112
  and mental retardation, 103
  and recovered memories, 44-46
  and repressed memories, 44-46, 55-59, 62-66, 69
  case studies, 38-40
  effect on the brain, 113, 115-116